HEALTH AND HEALING:

Ministry of the Church

**Papers presented at the Symposium
sponsored by
Wheat Ridge Foundation
at Yahara Retreat Center
Madison, Wisconsin**

March 10-14, 1980

Henry L. Lettermann, Editor

(Photography: Phyllis N. Kersten)

FOREWORD

Symposium on Health and Healing: Ministry of the Church!

Perhaps some would say there should be a question mark behind that statement. In this day of modern science and medicine, with all the expertise for organ transplants, all the sophistication challenging our society for a new definition of life and death, with all our drugs and medicines—and our much, much learning, should the church have anything at all to say about health and healing? Is the church really "out of its depth" on this one—should we leave it alone?

If modern medicine alone could assure everyone better health and a longer life, that would be one thing. But it cannot, nor does it make such a claim. With all the medical advances that have improved the quality of life in so many ways, still our society is not becoming all that more healthy. Many illnesses, especially those related to emotional stress, are on the increase. There is still something missing.

A group of Lutherans including health professionals, clergy, and laity came together the week of March 10-14, 1980, to explore this issue and to state with one voice: health and healing is very much the business of the church—and the church must get on with it.

This booklet has been printed for the purpose of sharing with you what took place that week at the Yahara Retreat Center near Madison, Wisconsin. But before we comment on the booklet itself, a word of explanation on how this meeting came about in the first place.

The seed of this symposium was planted 13 years ago (March 1967) in Coonoor, India. Here in a remote mountain setting a group of Lutherans, health professionals, missionaries and mission leaders, met to discuss this same topic—the healing ministry of the church—from a slightly different perspective. The Coonoor conference focused primarily on the theological basis for a healing ministry, particularly in the context of overseas mission work. But the Coonoor materials and papers are as fresh and relevant today as they were in 1967.

Building on that conference and using the occasion of its 75th anniversary as an opportunity to bring the subject closer to home, the Wheat Ridge Foundation decided to sponsor this 1980 symposium. Since Wheat Ridge has been involved in healing ministry since 1905—beginning with a TB sanitorium in Wheat Ridge, Colorado, and now as a channel for supporting a world-wide program in health and social ministry—it was a natural thing for Wheat Ridge to do. A Symposium steering committee of 12 persons was appointed in the summer of 1978 with representation from the American Lutheran Church, the Association of Evangelical Lutheran Churches, the Lutheran Church in America, the Lutheran Church—Missouri Synod, and the Wheat Ridge Foundation Board of Directors:

1. Dr. William H. Foege, Director, Center for Disease Control, Atlanta, Georgia
2. Dr. Ruth Goehle, furloughing medical missionary, on study leave in the U.S.
3. Dr. Helen Grace, Dean, School of Nursing, University of Illinois, Chicago, Illinois
4. Dr. Harold J. Hinrichs, Director for Personal and Group Life, ALC, Minneapolis, Minnesota
5. Dr. Richard F. Huegli, Executive Vice President, United Community Services of Metropolitan Detroit
6. Dr. Roland Miller, Academic Dean, Lutheran University, Regina, Saskatchewan
7. Mr. Neal F. Rabe, President, Concordia Mutual Life Association, Chicago, Illinois
8. Dr. Sidney Rand, President of St. Olaf College and now Ambassador to Norway
9. The Rev. Paul Strege, Project Director, Partners in Mission, St. Louis, Missouri
10. The Rev. Lee Wesley, Executive Director, Lutheran Community Services, New York
11. Mr. Robert J. L. Zimmer, President, Wheat Ridge Foundation, Chicago, Illinois
12. Dr. Robert P. Hopmann, Vice President, Wheat Ridge Foundation, Steering Committee Coordinator

The overall goal of the symposium was "to have North American Lutherans more actively engaged in Christ's healing ministry as individuals and together with others." The committee further determined to focus the discussion on North America and to emphasize practical application to the local congregation. The theme, "Health and Healing: Ministry of the Church," was chosen to convey the idea that the task involves preventive (health) and curative (healing) measures and that these activities are indeed an integral part of the church's ministry.

Participants, numbering approximately 100 from all across the U.S. and Canada, were selected by the steering committee in consultation with church judicatories. Four overseas representatives were invited as observers.

The sequence of the papers in this booklet follows the appearance of the presenters on the program. The papers were circulated prior to the symposium with Monday evening and Tuesday devoted primarily to "input" as each presenter was given time to highlight or summarize his/her paper. Wednesday was devoted to the presentation and discussion of six "action models," parish-based ministries that involve aspects of health and healing, summaries of which are included in this booklet. Thursday was set aside for the nine task groups to meet in workshop sessions in an effort to develop concrete recommendations for follow-up activity. Friday morning was devoted to hearing the results of the work done by the task groups; these reports are found at the back of the booklet.

Just a word about what happens now. Wheat Ridge is concerned that the work that went into this symposium will bear fruit at the congregational level. It is our hope and intention—with the help of the symposium participants, the good offices of the four church bodies, and the initiative of the many pastors who are already committed to this ministry—to promote the health and healing ministry of the local parish to the greatest extent possible. Several follow-up proposals are in the planning stages.

Finally, I would be remiss if I did not use this opportunity to thank some of those who contributed so much to making this symposium possible.

First a word of thanks to Mr. Neal F. Rabe, president of Concordia Mutual Life Association. Mr. Rabe and the CML Board of Directors had the vision and courage to see the need and to commit the Association to major financial support of the symposium and the follow-up publications. Through its fraternal benevolences program, Concordia Mutual Life has demonstrated an ongoing commitment to concerns of health and healing as ministries of the church.

Thanks must also go to Dr. Sidney Rand for his leadership as chairman of the steering committee prior to his appointment as ambassador to Norway, and to Dr. Richard Huegli who filled in for Dr. Rand and so ably chaired the week-long symposium. We are grateful to the entire steering committee for their time and diligence, to the three observer-reactors from Valparaiso University who served as a "rudder" during the week—Dr. Thomas Droege, Professor Lyle Franzen, and Deaconess Louise Williams; to our devotional leader, The Rev. Charles Mueller, for his daily spiritual guidance; and to all who took leadership roles as presenters or group leaders. We also express our appreciation to Dr. Henry Lettermann, English professor at Concordia College, River Forest, Illinois, for his work in editing and proofreading this booklet.

Last, but not least, a special word of thanks to the Wheat Ridge staff who were so involved and worked so hard over a period of three years for the success of this meeting: Dr. Robert P. Hopmann, who served as coordinator for the steering committee; Ms. Phyllis Kersten, Communications Director; and Ms. Juanita Tryman, Secretary.

Robert J. L. Zimmer
September 4, 1980

Contents

Dr. William H. Foege

CHAPTER I

Health and Healing: The Contemporary Scene

by William H. Foege

Americans have never been healthier, life expectancy has never been longer, and infant mortality has never been lower. Yet the newspapers
impress us with cancer rates that are increasing; we hear that chemicals
and food additives jeopardize our health, and that Americans are becoming
increasingly flabby. What is the truth about health? What is now being done?
What more could we do that is now left undone, and what should be our goals
for a healthy nation and a healthy world?

To understand where we are on the road to health, it is important to review
from whence we come.

It is a frequently repeated myth that in generations past, people had to do
all of their living between 20 and 30 years of age because they would die by age
35. In truth, where life expectancies were 35, this was due to high infant
mortality which influenced the average. In all cultures and in all generations,
children who have lived to adulthood have had a reasonable chance of living
into their 40's, 50's, and even 60's. Nevertheless, prior to 1900, the lives of
most people in most cultures were dominated by two factors: 1) infectious
diseases, and 2) violence.

Mention infectious diseases and we immediately think of the bubonic
plague; but, in fact, the terror of plagues was repeated on a small scale constantly. In our country, there are stories of entire wagon trains being wiped out
by cholera, battles won and lost because of infectious disease outbreaks; and in
the 1730's, New York City lost 7 percent of its population in a 90-day period
because of a smallpox outbreak.

Such dramatic events did not equal the total impact of day in-day out
losses of life due to infectious diseases. People lived in fear and violence.
Violence was the result of violent occupations, but more importantly the result
of intentional harm to others. By and large, the challenges of infectious diseases and violence were totally unmet by the medical profession, the church,
and society at large.

The last century has been marked by unbelievable progress against the
infectious diseases even though violence has continued to dominate the mor-

1

bidity-mortality scene. In 1900 (table 1), the leading causes of death in the United States were heavily influenced by infectious diseases. Indeed, when the question is raised in terms of years of life lost rather than absolute number of deaths (table 2), infectious diseases were four of the five leading causes. One by one, these ancient plagues yielded to medical knowledge and public health practice, resulting in dramatic reductions in tetanus, diphtheria, poliomyelitis, typhoid fever, etc. (tables 1, 2, and 3). So astonishing has been the change that diphtheria, the third leading cause of years lost in 1900, resulted in only three cases of disease in children under the age of 15 in the entire country in 1979.

The cumulative effect of each of these small victories has been an increase of over a quarter of a century in life expectancy for Americans in the 20th Century (table 4).

Even more remarkable is the relatively small part played by miracle drugs, highly technical surgical advances, and a $200 billion a year health care industry in increasing life expectancy. By and large, the changes can be credited to very simple and often poorly organized activities including improved housing, safe water supplies, waste disposal, regulations on food safety, environmental improvement, and immunization programs. These programs have had their primary effect on the reduction of infant and childhood mortality.

Indeed, David Rogers has said if we should lose all of our hospital beds overnight, it would not have the same influence on health as losing one of these simple preventive measures.

A current look at mortality shows a picture unimagined at the beginning of the century. Only a single infectious disease is still found in the ten leading causes of death (table 3). Not a single infectious disease is found in the five leading causes of years lost (table 4). But, it is striking how many of these five leading causes of years lost are potentially preventable. Violence still eludes our best control efforts. Accidents are largely preventable. Diseases of the cardiovascular system have shown significant declines in the last decade and are highly vulnerable to prevention procedures. While it is true that overall cancer rates have been increasing in this country, the fact is that non-cigarette induced cancers are declining and a major impact on cancer mortality could be made in this country simply by eliminating cigarette smoking.

These figures lead us to a sobering conclusion. I mentioned that life expectancy has increased by over a quarter of a century since 1900. But if we look only to life expectancy at my age (figure 6), I find that I can expect to live only six years longer than my grandfather's expectation at the same age because most of the increase in life expectancy has been due to a decrease in infant and childhood mortality. That means that at my age, all of 20th Century science and medicine can provide me only six more years as compared to my grandfather at the same age. On the other hand, Dr. Lester Breslow at the University of California has shown in Alameda County that some very simple life habits such as no smoking, drinking in moderation, exercise, and proper diet, can make a difference of ten or eleven years in the life expectancy of a person my age. In essence, what individuals do for themselves and to them-

2

selves can be twice as powerful as all of the benefits of 20th Century medicine. If this is true, then the major thrust of public health in the 1980's should be to exploit as a priority, the life-giving powers of the individual. This type of education—the development of good life habits, the equipping of individuals to make informed decisions—has not been a characteristic of the health care industry. We have historically looked to our families, our churches, and our education systems to instill such values and skills.

The advances of preventive medicine in the past decades have largely been elitist in the sense that decisions have been made by small groups to chlorinate water supplies, drain swamps, and regulate food preparation. The decisions have been carried out through social and environmental manipulation. The advances of the future will still involve some social and environmental manipulation as we attempt to reduce tar and nicotine levels in cigarettes, prevent the introduction of chemicals to our water supplies, etc. But the major disease prevention accomplishments for the remainder of this century will be seen in billions of decisions and actions taken by millions of people on a day-to-day basis. These include decisions to stop smoking, decisions to exercise daily, decisions to alter eating habits; decisions and actions so undramatic that they prompt most of us to say, ''Who cares?'' This is absolutely fertile ground for churches to take a leadership role by developing a church community that says we care and there are things that you can do.

This understanding of the importance of personal lifestyle in maintaining health raises the important question of how to provide individuals with usable information and how to incorporate church groups in implementation.

We have been testing a system at CDC over the past two years called Health Hazard Appraisal. The basic premise has been to provide individuals with personalized information about what certain actions could mean for them. A second objective has been to provide them with assistance in taking those actions. The Health Hazard Appraisal begins with a form on which the individual indicates present habits of smoking, drinking, seat belt use, family history, exercise habits, blood pressure, cholesterol levels, etc. The individual then receives a personalized form for comparing himself or herself to others of the same age group and quantifying the risks faced by the individual in the next 10 years as compared to other people. The printout also provides the individual with a realistic evaluation of his age. For instance, the form may indicate you are 43 years of age but your life habits indicate you are living as if you were 48. The printout continues, however, with a compliance age which is the age the person could be with certain lifestyle changes. The form may say you could be 39 again if you would do the following things. It appears to be much more powerful to tell people they can be 39 again rather than telling them they may extend their life span by 4 or 5 years. The form then lists the suggested actions to be undertaken and indicates the effect of each action so that a person can choose actions rather than make all reforms at once. The reforms are often closely related in the sense that it is very difficult to become a jogger without giving up smoking, losing weight, and having one's blood pressure decreased.

3

We have followed this examination at CDC by arranging for remedial actions such as Weight Watcher's, exercise classes, and smoking ending clinics. A recent survey of our employees showed that 70 percent indicated a change in one or more health habits in the past year. It remains to be seen if this change can be maintained. Interestingly, the same approach attempted with the adult group at church was less enthusiastically received probably because of the difficulty of devising remedial programs for small numbers, but also because of some underlying feelings that this was not the business of the church. I remain convinced this can be and will be a valuable health promotion device in the future and believe we should look to the successes of the Mormon Church and the Seventh Day Adventist Church in such endeavors. It is a fact that Mormons and Seventh Day Adventists live longer.

These observations raise serious questions regarding the ethical responsibility of the individual. What responsibility do I have to both society at large and to my own immediate family to maintain my health? What are the economic responsibilities? If cigarette smoking raises the national health care cost by $30 or $40 billion a year, should cigarette smokers be required to pay this increment?

What are the ethical implications for those who advocate unhealthy practices and indeed make their profits at the expense of others' health? In the days of tuberculosis, bubonic plague, and smallpox we were not faced with the dilemma of people promoting and profiting from the spread of an organism. It is clear that we would now look back with disgust if we were to learn that merchants made a profit from the spread of bubonic plague. Will we look back with similar disgust in 100 years and will our grandchildren question our intelligence when they learn that the great epidemic of the 20th Century, cigarette smoking, which killed 1,000 people per day in the United States, was being promoted by the profitmakers and that even children were being seduced through organized lying that promised unimaginable pleasures and abilities to attract the opposite sex?

In essence, the domestic health picture is one of rapid changes in the 20th Century; of a decrease in unnecessary morbidity and mortality, and evidence of an increase in the quality of life. Eighty percent of these gains have been achieved with perhaps 20 percent of the effort which has been placed in implementing simple prevention methods. The remaining small improvement has been achieved as the result of a massive health care system costing about $200 billion per year. But we now find ourselves in a unique situation. Considerable gains can be imagined in the next 20 years at relatively little cost, without a great expansion of technology if we return to the common sense that our grandmothers taught us, namely moderation in all things. To achieve this will require a cooperative venture involving millions and millions of people in this country. Churches have an obvious opportunity in this low technology return to prudence in living.

Meanwhile, what is the contemporary scene in the Third World? The Third World is also marked by a health revolution as they travel through their

4

first public health revolution similar in many ways to what happened in this country during the first half of the 20th Century. Throughout the world, infant mortality is decreasing, life expectancy is increasing, and birth rates are falling.

Life expectancy in the Third World is now at the level found in industrial countries in the 1920's and 1930's and could well reach 65-70 years by the year 2000. But the Third World has a double problem during the coming decades. It will continue to live with the historic problems of infectious diseases, malnutrition, and population pressures, but at the same time will increasingly become the victims of westernization. It is now facing the problems of occupational hazards and occupational exposures, the environmental problems of chemical wastes as well as the problems of affluence with which we are coping. Indeed, by the year 2000, the major health problem in the Third World will be the effects of cigarette smoking.

As we outline the problems of the Third World, the frequent question is: Why should we be concerned? Don't we already have overwhelming problems to deal with here? One reason is because we are a civilized society. How does the fact that we consider ourselves to be a civilized society fit in? I have recently, in a speech, explored the relationship between civilization and public health. A summary of that exploration is that civilization cannot be measured in terms of knowledge, ability to control our environment and destiny, technology, happiness, or freedom. The measure of civilization is ultimately found in how people treat each other. While we think of that in terms of the Golden Rule, Confucius put it even more succinctly when asked by his student, ''Is there one word which may serve as a rule of practice for one's life?'' Confucius considered the question and answered, ''Is not *reciprocity* such a word?'' Public health programs and prevention programs turn out to be good indices of how we treat other people. But the more geographically remote the target of a public health and prevention program is, the more difficult it is to develop interest, mobilize resources, and carry it out. Therefore, public health programs promoted by us in other countries indicate a high level of civilization. The corollary law would read the more remote the benefits in time, the more difficulty will be encountered in obtaining support for prevention programs. Therefore, one can conclude that the most civilized prevention programs possible are programs carried out for an audience unseen because of both time and geography. The U. S. demonstrates its level of civilization when it supports prevention programs in the Third World for the benefit of coming generations.

A second reason why we should be concerned is that we already have the experiences of dealing with the first public health revolution and we have current involvement in the second public health revolution. Therefore, we have much to offer. We have people who have dealt with clean water supplies, environmental sanitation, chemical wastes, and immunization programs. As humanitarians, we can't tolerate limited availability of lifesaving knowledge. Third, it's a good selfish investment. World peace in the time of our children or grandchildren is more likely to be seen in an environment of low morbidity,

5

low mortality, and low birth rates than in an unstable world with high mortality, high birth rates, and high illness rates. The church has had a great history of introducing medical care systems to developing countries. First it was felt through numerous isolated groups, and more recently through a heavy influence of the Christian Medical Commission of the World Council of Churches. It has molded individual medical activities and individual church activities into systems that have emphasized prevention, emphasized cooperation with other church groups, and emphasized coordination under government plans. Now it is time for churches to exercise their creativity to make individual congregations healing communities, both here and abroad; to take seriously the responsibility to provide individuals with the knowledge and motivation to take individual, family, and community actions which enhance health that all may have life more abundantly.

Table 1

TEN LEADING CAUSES OF DEATH
U.S.A., 1900

Information Reported
On Ten States

(ICDA—5th Revision)

Causes	Rate per 100,000
Pneumonia & Influenza	202.2
Tuberculosis	194.2
Diarrhea, Enteritis, and Ulceration of Intestines	142.7
Diseases of Heart	137.4
Intracranial Lesions of Vascular Origin	106.9
Nephritis	88.6
All Accidents	72.3
Cancer and Other Malignant Tumors	64.0
Senility	50.2
Diphtheria	40.3

Source: National Center for Health Statistics
HEW,PHS,CDC

Table 2

YEARS OF POTENTIAL LIFE LOST
U.S.A., 1900*

AGES 1—64		
Cause	**Total Years Lost**	**% of Total Years**
Tuberculosis	1,129,440	18.6
Influenza & Pneumonia	792,640	13.0
Diphtheria	433,997	7.1
All Accidents	404,567	6.7
Diarrhea & Enteritis	359,869	5.9

AGES 1—74		
Cause	**Total Years Lost**	**% of Total Years**
Tuberculosis	1,487,870	18.2
Influenza & Pneumonia	1,045,435	12.8
All Accidents	524,836	6.4
Diphtheria	508,908	6.2
Diseases of Heart	473,469	5.8

*Based on 10 States Reporting
Source: CDC, BSS, HAAPS
HEW, PHS, CDC

Table 3

TEN LEADING CAUSES OF DEATH
U.S.A., 1975

Information Reported
On Fifty States

(ICDA—8th Revision)

Causes	Rate per 100,000
Diseases of Heart	336.2
Malignant Neoplasms	171.7
Cerebrovascular Diseases	91.1
All Accidents	48.4
Influenza & Pneumonia	26.1
Diabetes Mellitus	16.5
Cirrhosis of Liver	14.8
Arteriosclerosis	13.6
Suicide	12.7
Certain Causes of Mortality in Early Infancy	12.5

Source: National Center for Health Statistics
HEW, PHS, CDC

Table 4

YEARS OF POTENTIAL LIFE LOST
U.S.A., 1975

AGES 1—64		
Cause	**Total Years Lost**	**% of Total Years**
All Accidents	2,589,552	25.1
Cancer	1,802,820	17.5
Diseases of Heart	1,769,180	17.2
Homicide	625,806	6.1
Suicide	588,276	5.7
AGES 1—74		
Cause	**Total Years Lost**	**% of Total Years**
Diseases of Heart	4,471,254	23.8
Cancer	3,841,801	20.5
All Accidents	3,408,455	18.1
Cerebrovascular Disease	869,352	4.6
Suicide	829,109	4.4

Source: CDC, BSS, HAPPS
HEW, PHS, CDC

Table 5

LIFE EXPECTANCY AT BIRTH

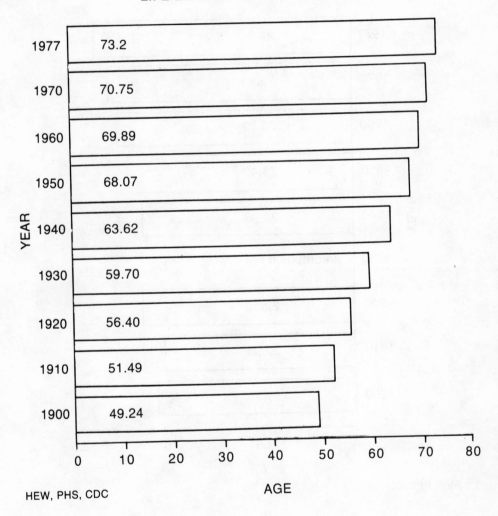

HEW, PHS, CDC

AGE

11

Table 6

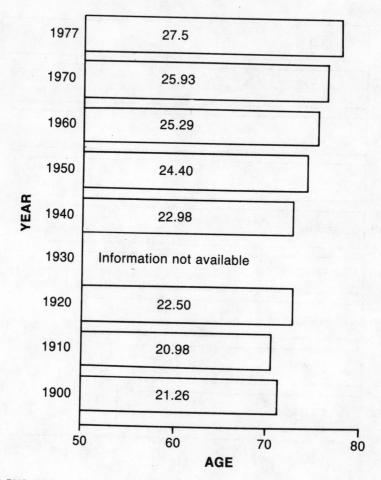

LIFE EXPECTANCY AT AGE 50

YEAR	AGE
1977	27.5
1970	25.93
1960	25.29
1950	24.40
1940	22.98
1930	Information not available
1920	22.50
1910	20.98
1900	21.26

HEW, PHS, CDC

Dr. Roland E. Miller

CHAPTER II

Christ The Healer

by Roland E. Miller

I greet you, healers of God in an ailing world, in the name of Christ the Healer!

I would like to take you on another walk along a well-travelled road. You may feel that there are few surprises left on this road, and perhaps you are right. My hope is, however, that in this walk the Risen Lord will meet you and make Himself known to you again, that He will interpret Himself to you freshly, that He will cause your hearts to burn within you. That somewhat audacious hope is one that I can hold because I believe that He will be breaking the bread of fellowship with us as we journey together through these hours and days. He who began the mission of healing will help us with His presence and grace as we try to understand it more truly and obey it more purely.

To that end, I wish to put before you the vision of the Healing Christ, and ask you to contemplate what you see.

A generous Wheat Ridge Foundation news release indicated that I would be delivering a major theological paper, presumably helping to lay a theological base for the healing ministry of the church. Partly because I quail and feel rather helpless before such a formidable task, partly because I feel that at this jucture we must focus our minds on the essentials, I am deliberately drawing in the limits of this discussion. Important as it is, I will not be trying to sketch a broadly inclusive philosophy of healing. Essential as it is, I will not be deliberating upon a total Christian theology of healing. I will not be trying to draw out the comprehensive Biblical basis of healing, nor even the full New Testament theology of healing. I am interested, rather, in looking with you at the Healing Christ.

To do this, I think, is to take seriously our theological concern and task. In fact, that focus goes to the heart of theology itself. The core of theology (words about God) has to do with Jesus Christ (the Word of God). What we call the theology of the church is reflection upon Him, and upon what has been revealed and wrought through Him. Theology in this narrow concentrated sense leads to theology in the broad systematic sense. As you translate the vision of Christ into the theory and practice of parish healing this week, you will be working on a broad theology of healing. But the starting-point is clear. We cannot think healing or do healing without steadfastly gazing upon the Figure of Him Who is the Author and Finisher of our healing as well as our faith.

15

I will attempt to deal with the topic in two major sections: Part A on Christ and Healing, and Part B on Christ the Healer. The distinction is arbitrary, but roughly parallels the use of a broad brush and a fine brush by a painter. I will not try to spell out in any detail the meaning of the picture that emerges in terms of specific applications to the healing ministry of Christian congregations in the 1980's. That constructive task I leave to you—I take it to be the very purpose of this conference.

A. CHRIST AND HEALING

1. The Cosmic Context

Summary: Healing is an aspect of the total movement of the redemptive love of God.

Let us get a sense of the grand design of the God of the universe. You must see yourself and set your ministry in the cosmic context of the healing God. I heard Krister Stendahl say:[1] "God's agenda is the mending of creation." I liked that then, and still do. As my salutation to you I could have said, I greet you, menders of creation in a broken world, in the name of the Mender!

Mending is an expression for God's total movement of creative love toward suffering humanity, of which healing is an aspect. From the beginning of time that movement of love was associated with the Word of God.

> It was through him that all things came into being, and without him came nothing that has come to be. In him there was life, and that life was the light of men.[2]

In a sense, we can say that the healing light of Jesus Christ has always been in the world, as a ray of His life-giving and sustaining Presence. When from the Greek genius Hippocrates (400 B.C.) there poured forth that oath which binds doctors to this day, he was responding to that hidden Light. When Ibn Sina (= Avicenna, d. 1135), the illustrious Arab Muslim philosopher-theologian-physician composed his "Poem of Medicine" and systematized the entire medical knowledge of his day, he was responding to that Light. When a Hindu ayurvedic practitioner in village India today ministers to and restores the sense of physical well-being of the nation's President, with his combination of herbal treatment and oil massage, he is responding to that Light.[3] God's active goodness pervades the universe, inspiring every form of human goodness, and His footprints are impressed on the sands of life for those who have eyes to see.

---

[1] Stendahl was speaking at a seminar at Luther College, University of Regina, Regina, Saskatchewan, Canada, March 1, 1979.

[2] Most of the Biblical quotations are taken from the translation of the New Testament by Monsignor Ronald A. Knox (London: Burns & Oates, 1958).

[3] Former India President V. V. Giri regularly visited the small Kerala village of Kottakkal for treatment at its famed Ayurvaidyasala.

Yet the darkness does not comprehend it, or apprehend it. So in the fullness of time the Sun of Righteousness Himself appeared, "with healing in his wings."[4] The Light of God was condensed into one solitary incandescent flame, of infinite intensity and power, the true burning and shining light that can lighten every human being that comes into the world.

> And the Word was made flesh and came to dwell among us, and we had sight
> of His glory, glory as belongs to the Father's only-begotten Son, full of
> grace and truth.[5]

He veiled that Light in human form so that we could see it and live, could share it and give. Some looked and saw only an earthly flicker, the human form of Joseph's son, and they were repelled and received nothing. Others saw in Him what we all are intended to see, the fullness of God in His self-giving, life-bestowing Reality.

> It was God's good pleasure to let all completeness dwell in him, and through
> him to win back all things, whether on earth or in heaven, into union with
> himself, making peace with them through his blood shed on the cross.[6]

In Jesus Christ the saving God went forth to save. In Him the Lord of all reclaimed His universe, and established the new situation of healing and hope in which we live.

He is the Light of the world. I do not want to teach you about Jesus Christ—as though I could!—I want you to look at the light, which embodies everything that God wishes to communicate to us and make possible for us, and

> go on, then, ordering your lives in Christ Jesus our Lord . . . (for) in Christ
> the whole plenitude of Deity is embodied, and dwells in him, and it is in him
> that you find your completion; he is the fountainhead from which all
> dominion and power proceeds.[7]

As we look at that Flame and go on ordering our lives in response to it, the Light enters us. For God who commanded the Light to shine out of darkness "has kindled a light in our hearts, whose shining is to make known his glory as he has revealed it in the features of Jesus Christ."[8] Filled with this Light we now understand, we have power, we desire to live, to love, to proclaim, to recreate, to heal; we have, miracle of miracles!, a share in both the mind of God and the possibility of God.

> Risen with Christ you must live your thoughts above. . . . You have under-
> gone death, and your life is hidden away now with Christ in God. . . . There
> is nothing but Christ in any of us.[9]

---

[4]Mal. 4:2.
[5]Jn. 1:14.
[6]Col. 1:19-20.
[7]Col. 2:9.
[8]1 Cor. 4:6.
[9]Col. 3:1.

17

The Christ-connection not only enables us to walk in the light, brightening and warming the world, but it is the guarantee that we shall share in its final revelation. It is then that the weak old order in which we suffer and heal, heal and suffer, shall have passed away, and the Lamb shall be the lamp of the city of God, by Whose light the nations shall walk, and Whom they shall praise and adore as King of Kings and Lord of Lords. The total movement of redemptive love shall reach its culmination when He hands over the Kingdom to His Father and takes His seat at His right hand.

> Full completion comes . . . when he places his kingship in the hands of God, his Father, having first dispossessed every sort of rule, authority and power; his reign as we know must continue until he has put all enemies under his feet, and the last of those enemies to be dispossessed is death. God has put all things in subjection under his feet . . . so that God may be all in all.[10]

In this brief sketch I have attempted to evoke rather than to describe our sense of participation in a cosmic drama of redemption and re-creation. The mending of creation has been underway since the moment the life of humanity was fractured, and at its centre stands Christ the Healer. Those who follow Him are part of that grand design. They are caught up in it. Christian healers are not an isolated, special-interest group. Defensive attitudes, building up our concerns by downing others, pressure tactics, mystery production, mutual ego stroking—all the worst characteristics of such groups have no place among us. If present, they stem from a lack of sense of the grand design and our part in it. We are members of the Body of Him by Whom all things were made and towards Whom all things head, His people on His mission, the signs and builders of His Kingdom on earth until He comes. Only, St. Paul says, "Let each man take care how he builds . . . for no other foundation can anyone lay than that which is laid in Jesus Christ. . . . You are for Christ, and Christ is for God."[11]

So let us learn from Him how to build the Kingdom. From the cosmic drama we must go to the vision of the One Who walked among us. He is the foundation of every aspect of Christian obedience, including the ministry of healing. He promised that we would do greater works than He, and it is clear that He demands no slavish repetition but rather a lively and creative response to His Spirit. Yet there can be no argument that our approach to the healing task, both in spirit and in practice, must be drawn from the Healing Christ. At the beginning of His ministry Jesus once asked some men, "What will you have of me?" When they told Him, He said, "Come and see." The context was different but the words are appropriate at the beginning of our planning for this decade.

"What will you have of me?"

"Lord, show what it means to heal."

"Come and see!"

[10] 1 Cor. 15:24ff.
[11] 1 Cor. 3:9-11, 23.

18

Summary: Healing has a spontaneous character that results from association with the free and unpremeditated love of God.

There is a natural quality to Christian healing that we must catch.

Jesus Christ's healing ministry is set in the context of His total communication of the love of God. He does not treat it as a special ministry requiring special attention. It is a natural expression of what the God-related person is and does. It is the inevitable reflex of love. As I read the Gospels again in this connection, I tried to expose myself to their message in a somewhat impressionistic way. One thing that I came away with was a sense of the natural, spontaneous quality of Christ's healing. It did not have a super-honed programmatic character, but rather the lively quality of *agape*, the unconditioned love of God, which was in Him responding to human need of every variety. His healing seemed to be part of His living and breathing in God. He had an on-going sense of being one with the Father. As a result, He identified His will with God's, and His commitment to that will, which He understood as love, was as natural as eating and drinking. "My food is to do the will of Him that sent me."[12]

Jesus frequently used the picture of a fruit-bearing tree to underline the natural quality of this response. At the same time, there is no suggestion that spontaneity equates to lack of awareness. His own obedience was not unconscious, machine-like. He knew very well what He was doing and was ready to discuss it. His discussion did not stultify the spontaneity of His response, however, as our discussions and plannings sometimes seem to do. I think it was because He always kept a sense of the relationship from which His obedience flowed. He always pointed to the spring from which He drank. "The Father loves the Son, and discloses to him all that he himself does."[13] This conscious sense of direct linkage with the dynamic love of God gave alertness and awareness to the life and ministry of the Healer. That quality too He passes on to His followers.

> My Father's name has been glorified if you yield abundant fruit and prove yourselves my disciples. I have bestowed my love upon you, just as my Father has bestowed his love upon me; live on in my love. You will live on in my love if you keep my commandments."[14]

Neither does this natural quality of the life of love mean that it is aimless. Spontaneity is not to be identified with lack of direction. The spontaneous life of love can be ordered with plans and purpose. We see that reflected in God's own plan for the mending of creation. The sense of purpose was very prominent in Jesus. Note the phrase that comes at the end of the passage quoted earlier. "My food is to do the will of him that sent me, *and to complete his work.*" He maintained this sense of objective throughout His career.

[12]Jn. 4:34.
[13]Jn. 5:20
[14]Jn. 15:8ff.

Do not think that I have come to set aside the law and the prophets; I have not come to set them aside but to bring them to perfection.[15]

I must go up to Jerusalem.

I have glorified thee on earth. I have finished the work thou gavest me to do. . . . It is finished.[16]

Spontaneous love is not only alert, but sets out to do things, and finishes them.

3. The Unnatural Quality: Sent to Love

Summary: Healing has a deliberate and burden-bearing character that results from the sending of God.

There is an unnatural quality to Christian healing that we must recognize.

If love is natural, spontaneous, outgoing, we may well ask, why is it that it must be commanded? If light shines naturally, why must it be ordered to shine? Yet it is commanded.

Your light must shine so brightly before men that they can see your good works and glorify your Father who is in heaven.[17]

Why is this word needed? We might also ask, why do we need this meeting at all to talk about something so obvious as the healing ministry? The question may be pressed farther with reference to the Healer Himself. I am struck by Christ's sense of being sent by God. I have counted 26 times in St. John's Gospel alone where He mentions that He has been sent, and there may be more. It is clear that this fact dominated His thoughts. We must ask, however, why free-flowing Love needed sending, and why the sending was so important to Him.

I do not propose to find the answer to the question in the truth that we are at the same time saints and sinners. That truth is applicable to us but has nothing to do with the Christ. Rather I find the answer in the character of evil itself. There is a forbidding quality about evil, evil of any kind. It is horrible. It disgusts and contaminates. The average person is repelled by it. Nothing reveals its shocking nature better than the famous story of Gautama Buddha's first encounter with evil.[18]

Buddha had been secluded by his royal father from every contact with evil and suffering. One day the young prince drove forth from his palace with his charioteer and saw a peculiar sight. On inquiring about it, he was informed that he had just seen a man of great age, and that youth must ever yield to age. Thereupon he cried, "Shame then on life, since the decay of every living thing is notorious." Later he saw a sick man, thin and weak with

---

[15]Mt. 5:17.
[16]Jn. 17:4; 19, 30.
[17]Mt. 5:16.
[18]Cf. Ananda K. Coomaraswamy, *Buddha and the Gospel of Buddhism* (New York: Harper & Row, 1964), pp. 19f. The religion of Buddhism, an effort to deal with the problem of suffering, sprang from this encounter.

fever. When the meaning of the spectacle was made clear to him, he cried, "If health be frail as the substance of a dream, who then can take delight in joy and pleasure?" A third time he ventured forth, and for the first time he saw a corpse being carried through the streets. After the charioteer had explained the significance of the weeping and the beating of breasts Buddha cried: "Woe to the life so soon ended! Would that sickness, age and death might be forever bound! Turn back again, that I may seek a way of deliverance!"

If evil repels ordinary human beings to this extent, how much more repelling is it to absolute goodness! There are two possible reactions for goodness in the face of evil. Neutrality is not one of them. Either goodness senses its incompatibility with evil, is wounded and distressed by the sight of it, is repelled and withdraws from contact with it. Or goodness draws near to evil and seeks to overcome it. I suggest that both reactions are proper to goodness, and this in part explains why it was necessary that Jesus be sent, and that we be commanded to heal.

On the one hand God separates Himself from evil—and His separation is the judgment upon it. To be separate from evil is natural for the Holy One Who is "majestic in holiness." On the other hand God enters the sphere of evil, draws near to it, yes even becomes identified with evil in order to overcome it.[19] That is the "unnatural" thing for God to do. There is strain in it. There is temptation in it. There is suffering in it. So God Who naturally recoils from evil sends Himself. The Son of Love Who would naturally go must nevertheless be sent into the arena of the evil one. It is evident that it was this sense of being sent by the Father that enabled Jesus Christ to maintain His commitment in His traumatic and unnatural encounter with evil and suffering. "O my Father, if it be possible, let this cup pass from me: nevertheless not as I will, but as thou wilt. . . . O my Father, if this cup may not pass from me except I drink it, thy will be done."[20] The Sent One drank the cup. Goodness engaged with evil in mortal combat, and in that battle death is swallowed up in victory.

Even so Christ the Healer sends us. He sends us to the unnatural thing, to be in contact with evil, to be involved with sickness and suffering. He commands us to heal. He knows that we require His commission, and gives it. We do not only love, but we are sent to love.

And preach as you go, telling them, the kingdom of God is at hand. Heal the sick, raise the dead, cleanse the lepers, cast out devils: give as you have received the gift, without payment.[21]

Only those who believe that they have been sent by God to do battle with evil will be able to drink the cup that He drank, and to give as they have received.

[19] Cf. 2 Cor. 5:21.

[20] Mt. 26:39, 42.

[21] Mk. 10:17.

Summary: Healing has an integral place in the whole mission of God and the fulfillment of His will.

From all that has been said the integral relation of mission and healing is evident. The mending of creation, which is God's agenda, the all-encompassing movement of love, the engagement with evil, these leave nothing out of their scope and certainly not what we commonly call healing.[22]

In St. Matthew 3:19 the Lord gives His classic call: "Come, follow me, and I will make you fishers of men." Then, in the next verses (23ff.) He provides His personal exegesis of that call.

> So Jesus went about the whole of Galilee teaching in their synagogues, preaching the good news of the kingdom, and curing every kind of disease and infirmity among the people. . . . And they brought to him all those who were in affliction, distressed with pain and sickness of every sort, the possessed, the lunatics, the palsied, and he healed them.

The rhythm of preaching, teaching, and healing runs all the way through the Messiah's ministry. Those who came to Him reflected that rhythm, for they came "to listen to him and to be healed of their diseases."[23] When Jesus made his striking and compelling declaration, "I must work the works of Him that sent me; the night is coming when there is no working any more,"[24] He uttered it in the context of the healing of the man born blind.

We have been reminded repeatedly in this present age that Jesus Christ is the Prince of Peace, the King of Shalom. The word *shalom,* which carries the inclusive sense of total well-being, is translated in the New Testament by *eirene,* peace. Originally the Greek term *eirene* really meant the absence of conflict. It is used sometimes in that sense in the New Testament, and is especially important in conveying the idea that the warfare between God and man has ended because of Christ, and a new relationship has come into being. But very often *eirene,* peace, is filled with the Old Testament meaning of

---

[22]Christian healers often wonder why there is not wider recognition of healing in the program of the church. In this area it is well to avoid on the one hand the Scylla of judgmentalism, since in fact many Christians are engaged in healing ministries, in with and under their daily life. On the other hand, the Charybdis of immobilization also needs avoiding, for we may be so preoccupied with the fact of neglect and its causes that we lose sight of our function. It is true, of course, that very few congregations of the church have engaged themselves with the question of their healing mission, which *is* a matter of great concern. The church has revealed a tendency to be more alert to one dimension of its task while ignoring others in various periods of its development. In the Reformation age, for example, Protestant Christians had very little consciousness of the global mission of the church. Some even argued that the apostolic command to go into all the world had been fulfilled! It was not till 1706 that the first Protestant missionary (Ziegenbalg) arrived in India, and it was not until the 19th century that we reached "the great century" of mission. It is part of the task of healers—and it will be a continuing one—to minister to the inadequate understanding and implementation of this aspect of God's mission. It should be pointed out that the church has typically been responsive to strong leadership from its midst.

[23]Lu. 6:18; cf. Mt. 7:29—8:1; 19:1-2.

[24]Jn. 9:4.

shalom, the total restoration of the true state of humanity. That thought is present both at the beginning of Jesus' life when the angels sang "peace on earth" and at the end when he wept over Jerusalem: "Ah, if thou too couldest understand, above all in this day that is given thee, the way that can bring thee peace."[25]

Between those terminals of His ministry Jesus sought to establish that *shalom*. His mission was expressed in the famous words of Isaiah that foretold the mandate of the Messiah.[26]

> He has anointed me and sent me out to preach the gospel to the poor, to restore the broken-hearted, to bid the prisoners to go free, to set the oppressed at liberty, to proclaim a year when men may find acceptance with the Lord, a day of retribution.

His acts of healing fall within that total *shalom* ministry, and are a sign of it. To the woman with the problem of bleeding the Healer said, "My daughter, thy faith has brought thee recovery; go in peace *(eirene)* and be rid of thy affliction."[27] We have not reached and may never attain to the full significance of that term, *shalom*. Later disciples saw it as the proper description of His ministry on earth. Peter said, "God has sent His word . . . giving them news of peace *(eirene)* though Jesus Christ who is Lord of all,"[28] and Paul asks us to be ready "to publish the God of peace *(eirene)*."[29]

Christ the Healer asks us to do the same. The passage, "Blessed are the peace-makers"[30] has been almost universally interpreted as an encouragement to disciples to help in solving conflicts. I am not at all minded to lose that significance, especially in view of the conflicts in our world today. But I cannot help but think that this beatitude may have depths we have not plumbed. "Blessed are the shalom-makers, the builders of total well-being," is what it may be saying. To make that kind of total ministry possible He gives His *shalom* to His disciples: "Peace I leave with you, my peace I give to you,"[31] a peace that is connected with His resurrection victory and power. It was when He showed them the scars in His hands and side, the healed wounds, the signs of the enemy overcome, that He said, "Peace be unto you." Then to make clear that we have His powerful *shalom* to give to others, He declared again: "Peace be with you; as my Father sent me, so send I you."[32]

5. *The Kingdom and the Power: Healing and the Rule of God*

Summary: Healing is a sign of the rule of God, active among us now and still to be revealed.

---

[25]Lu. 19:41.
[26]Lu. 4:18; cf. Is. 61:1-2.
[27]Mk. 5:34.
[28]Acts 10:36.
[29]Eph. 6:15.
[30]Mt. 5:9.
[31]Jn. 14:27.
[32]Jn. 5:20.

23

Jesus Christ declared, "The time is fulfilled, and the kingdom of God is at hand: repent ye, and believe the gospel."[33] This was His first public word, and it initiated a constant theme in His ministry. The kingdom of God has been described as the central theme of His life and message. Kingdom of God means the reign or the rule of God. Alan Richardson explains the above passage in the following words:[34]

> In general terms, this means that Jesus proclaimed as good news the fact that God was setting about the task of putting straight the evil plight into which the world had fallen, or that He was beginning to bring to its fulfillment his original intention in the Creation.

God's reign is here. That which prophets and kings had longed to see is present. God has visited and redeemed His people. The day is at hand. The merciful kindness of our God has dawned upon us to give light to those who live in darkness, in the shadow of death, and to guide our feet into the way of *shalom*. The testimony to the fullness of time is Jesus Christ Himself, and His words and works. When John the Baptist wondered whether it was He or not, Jesus said: "Go, tell John . . . how the blind see, the lame walk, and the lepers are made clean, and the deaf hear; how the dead are raised to life, and the poor have the gospel preached to them."[35] Tell him that the kingdom has arrived.

This is the appropriate point to say a word about the miracles of the Christ, especially the healing miracles. Most obviously they were His response to need. But they were more than that. They were signs of the kingdom. They were the signal that the time had come for God to put in His hand, to enter the fray, to personally and powerfully take on the forces of evil. They were not spectacles, intended for oohs and ahs or for personal advance. They were rather the signs that a decisive attack was underway and that the age of salvation had now begun. Like all signs, they were meant to be read. They were the "enacted proclamation" of the kingdom of God, and called for response. They testified not simply that the kingdom had come, but that it had come in Jesus. Thus they were at the same time evidence of His Messiahship and a call to faith. He said, "If when I cast out devils I do it through the Spirit of God, then it must be that the kingdom of God has already appeared among you;"[36] and He reproached the impenitence of the communities in which He had performed most of His wonders: "Tyre and Sidon would have repented in sackcloth and ashes long ago, if the miracles done in you had been done there instead."[37]

The healing miracles, then, had a special function related to the pioneer ministry of Jesus the Messiah. He shared this authority with the twelve (Lu. 9:1) and with the seventy (Lu. 10:9) as signs to them. They were the strong overture needed to introduce the symphony of witness. There is no indication

---

[33]Mk. 1:15.
[34]*Theological Wordbook of the Bible* (New York: Macmillan, 1950), p. 119.
[35]Lu. 7:22.
[36]Mt. 12:28.
[37]Mt. 11:20.

24

that the miracles of healing were to go on as a widespread, permanent feature in the church, or that the healing miracles of the Christ were to be emulated by the mass of His followers. The great, comprehensive commissions of the Master to His disciples[38] are devoid of reference to this theme. It is significant that in his list of the gifts of the Spirit, St. Paul separates the gift of healing and the gift of miracles.[39] The two things do not automatically go together. The building of the kingdom and the establishment of its shalom will not be effected through wonder-working, but through suffering love. The royalty of the King is the royalty of self-giving love. Right at the start of His career Jesus in the wilderness turned His back on miracle methodology as the way of the kingdom. Not by turning stones into loaves of bread, but rather by living contact with God through His Word would His kingdom come.

There is one thing more, however, that remains to be said. Where Jesus did exert His divine power in those commanding demonstrations of authority, He exerted it most frequently and most forcefully among the sick. The kingdom of God is the kingdom of love, and its power is for others. The royal Healer's power was for others, and those others who most needed it were the sick and the handicapped, the poor and the oppressed. So power went out from the Healer. *Everything* that He was and *everything* that He had was offered up to the suffering human beings that He encountered. Therein, *in His holding nothing back,* is the sufficient lesson of the miracles of healing.

B. CHRIST THE HEALER

Let us look more closely at the Healer.

Jesus has meant many things to different people at various stages in the history of the church. In His day, Jesus the Messiah . . . in the early church, Jesus the Lord and Son of God . . . in medieval times, Jesus the Spiritual Master . . . in the Reformation period, Jesus the loving Saviour . . . in the nineteenth century, Jesus the Teacher . . . in the twentieth century, Jesus the Example and Authentic Human . . . in the present time, Jesus the Liberator. When will the world see Jesus the Healer? Perhaps we are near that time now. To show the Healer and to follow Him on His healing way is the task that faces the church in an increasingly disillusioned, fragmented, and troubled world.

See Him . . . See Him . . . is the strong, reverberating antiphony of a great Bach double chorus. It seems to say what we must be saying to the churches. Those who seek to engage the church afresh with the Healer and His tasks, however, must first see Him for themselves.

---

[38]Mt. 24:14; 28:19; Mk. 13:10; Lu. 24:47; Acts 1:8.

[39]1 Cor. 12:9-10. I have therefore chosen not to deal with the difficult and disputed matter of "faith healing" in this essay. That, I believe, has more to do with the continuation of special powers under the charisma of miracle working, rather than having to do with the charisma of healing. I realize that this is a border-line area and that not everyone will find the distinction valid.

See the focussed Healer.

There is no mystery about His ministry. It is so accessible to our observation. He was, and is, so real. After all the volumes have been written on that subject, He remains the epitome of down to earth practicality and concrete obedience. He was, in a sense, so narrow. He focussed on sick people, and healed them. Many heard about His concentrated attack on physical disease and demonic power, and they thronged about Him, bringing their ailing and distressed. Christ the Healer responded to them. Though we see Him withdrawing at times, we never see Him ignoring. Again and again we read the phrase, "and he healed every kind of disease and infirmity." "Great multitudes followed Him, and He healed all their diseases."[40] In discussing the attitude of Jesus toward evil, J. B. Phillips states that "His particular genius lies in concentration upon what is really essential." That is, He does not discourse about the origin of evil and suffering, but rather He accepts the human situation, focusses on the core realities, and deals with them.[41]

There is some reason to emphasize this point in view of the current stress on holism, that is, a broadly comprehensive view of the healing task. This development followed upon a new appreciation of the fact that an individual human being is an interactive totality of body and mind and soul, emotion and will, together with a new awareness of the fact that the health of human beings in community is affected by almost every condition and influence that runs through corporate life. These discoveries brought new depth and breadth to the understanding of the healing task. We must also ask, however, whether and to what extent the development represents a movement away from the focussed Healer.

A minor question relates to the language usage that has developed. I am mildly concerned about the jargon that is turning the healing ministry into an arcane mystery for ordinary Christians at a time when they are to be challenged to involvement and action. The term, "holism," for example, is very much the property of the few. Even dictionaries have not yet caught up to its usage connected with healing.[42] Of greater significance is its effect on the average person in the church; try out the term on a fellow member of your congregation and observe if you receive much more than a blank stare! From time to time every discipline needs self-examination and a modicum of reform at this point, since we all suffer from what Max Müller called "the disease of language." Is it possible, however, that we may have to consciously revert to the concrete language of the Healer Himself if we wish to move the church?

A larger question relates to the concept of holism itself. I am wondering to what extent it has inadvertently introduced a diluting effect upon healing, so that the latter has lost much of its distinctive meaning and power. If I may use

---

[40]Mt. 12:15.

[41]*God our Contemporary* (New York: Macmillan, 1960), p. 102.

[42]My unabridged Random House Dictionary (c. 1967) lists the term only in connection with a philosophic theory. Dictionaries of the last decade have slightly expanded the meaning.

an analogy—a rushing stream when it overflows its banks and spills into a broad, flat valley, no longer sustains its power and soon becomes a placid pool. The phenomenon that has taken place with respect to healing has a parallel in what has occurred with respect to the concept "mission." The latter has been so broadened as to include every aspect of Christian obedience, and as a result it has partially lost the force of the root idea of sending.[43]

While the adjective "holistic" attached to healing conveys a powerful meaning, it must be emphasized for the sake of definition that holistic ministry and healing ministry are not co-terminous. Healing ministry is an aspect of the shalom creation, and is not identical with it. All of life is interrelated and plays on health. The conclusion that since everything is somehow interlinked, the healing ministry must deal with every link in the chain does not follow, however; neither is it possible. Healing has to do with everything, but that does not imply that it must do everything. The area of healing ministry that crystallizes the problem under discussion is the field of preventive medicine which, by its very nature, has an inclusive concern. We faced this problem as we developed our Community Health Project at Malappuram, South India, with the assistance of the Wheat Ridge Foundation and Canadian Lutheran World Relief. Water supply, latrines, health education, nutrition, gardens, job-training, loans— you name it—we incorporated it all into a promising pilot project with the object of a healthier community and the goal of replication. The project is still continuing, and is in good health.[44] Since I believe that there is a place for that kind of ministry, both as a contribution to the building of health and as a signal of *shalom,* I would do it again. Yet I must admit that the true sign of the kingdom for the Mappila Muslims of Kerala, and that which has enabled some of them to see Christ and to follow Him, has been the focussed care of the sick in the name of the Healer that has been carried out over the years in that part of the world.

An interesting parallel to the dilution problem from outside the Christian tradition is the Gandhian Hindu concept of Sarvodaya, advanced by his great followers, Vinobha Bhave (*bhūdan,* land-gift movement) and the recently-deceased Jaya Prakash Narayan (*gram raj,* village power), as well as by the Indian government through its community development programs. Sarvodaya means total (*sarv*) well-being (*daya*). It includes every aspect of concern that Christians attach to the achievement of total health, with the exception of sin-sickness. A congress of Sarvodaya adherents several years ago identified the following as the ten basic goals for village communities: [45a] clean environment, water, clothing, a balanced diet, housing, basic health care, communication facilities, fuel, education, and the satisfaction of spiritual and cultural needs. Despite great efforts to make this a practical program, however, in part

---

[43]I have dealt with this development in a chapter ("Missions Tomorrow") in a forthcoming volume, *The Sending of God.*

[44]The directors of the program are Dr. Victoria Mathews and Mr. Tharyan Mathews.

[45a]Mt. 13:15; Jn. 12:40.

because of its utopian scope it has remained the concern of the few, and its impact has been effective primarily in societally isolated village areas. There is obviously great symbolic significance in movements such as these in an increasingly fragmented society, and they deserve recognition and praise. Their problems, however, speak to our basic question of how we should follow the focussed Healer.

I will return us then to the vision of the Healer, and the specificity I see in that vision. The term healing as used in the Gospels has concreteness and particularity. Its object is always sick persons, not circumstantial conditions. You may ask, does the figurative use, including the wider sweep of human ills, not appear? The broad, figurative sense of healing is found in the Old Testament, but it is not the mark of New Testament usage and does not represent the language of the Healer Himself. The only time the term "healing" is used in the broadly inclusive sense in the Gospels is in a quotation of an Old Testament passage.[45b] Elsewhere and everywhere it is severely focussed on the overcoming of disease. Albrecht Oepke[46] puts it in blunt words: "Physical healings dominate the field of vision." For the Healer that certainly included also the root of physical disease, the sin of humanity, which it was His mission to overcome. It is suggested, in fact, that the uniqueness of His healing rests in the way that "it embraces the outer and inner in man."[47]

What shall we say about the focussed Christ as we chart our objectives for parish healing? Does His concentration on the care of the sick reflect the limitations of His time? Is this too restricted a vision for healing in our day? Are not the wholesome aspects of holistic healing perhaps endangered thereby, so that we stand to lose everything we have gained through that understanding? I do not regard this focus of the Healer as a threat to the basic principle of holism, but rather as a challenge to a renewed acceptance of a fundamental function and to the development of clear objectives. Christ's ministry to sick persons was a concentration on an aspect of *shalom* that needed to be done in His day and needs doing today. Holistic theology means that we have a conscious sense of the wholeness of the church and the diversity of its gifts; in that light, it is possible, for example, that we should allow Christian economists, businessmen, and government servants, the sent ones of God in their situations, to minister to primary economic conditions that admittedly affect the standard of health. All similar vocational ministries need recognition and maximizing by the church. As our priority for the healing ministry of parishes, however, perhaps we should return to the physically sick. Are they not there? I do not know where it will take us in our practical decisions, but the vision of Christ beckons us on. Without being simplistic, antiquated, or fundamentalist

---

[45b]Quoted from R. MacGilliwray, "Religious Populism Rises in Sri Lanka," in *Connections* (Nov./Dec., 1979), p. 5.

[46]Gerhard Kittel, ed. *Theological Dictionary of the New Testament.* Vol. III (Grand Rapids: Eerdmans, 1965), p. 204. Oepke's article on *iaomai* and the article on *therapeuo*, both signifying "to heal," are fundamental sources for this study.

[47]*Ibid.*, p. 212.

in our understanding of either sickness or healing, without lowering our own commitment to general justice, without failing to recognize the value of all programs that contribute widely to the improvement of human conditions, we are clearly called to follow the Healer Who healed the sick.

2. See His Attitude

See Him . . . See Him . . .

He noticed.

He was alert, He looked for the sick, and He noticed them. As He passed the pool of Bethsaida "Jesus *saw* him (a disabled man) lying there."[48] He didn't have to see him, but He did.

He stopped.

That noticing was not a passing by on the other side or a clinically detached observer attitude. He responded to what He saw. He took the initiative and acted. Surrounded by the teeming throngs as He left Jericho on His way to His final entrance to Jerusalem, 16 miles away, two blind persons came to His attention. The sight caused Him to bring to a halt a cosmically significant journey. "Then Jesus *stopped* and called to them."[49]

He was horrified.

He was horrified at what He saw. The suffering and sadness He encountered was not the intention of God. Abraham Heschel observes that modern man is brutalized and has lost his sense of horror.[50] Our horror is covered by celluloid. We have seen too much, so what we see no longer moves us. When they brought the deaf and dumb man to Jesus in Decapolis, "he looked up and sighed."[51] But the word that is usually translated as sighing (*stenazo*) is the same as the one used in the New Testament to signify the groaning of creation.[52] Jesus groaned.

He was angry.

He was not only horrified but angry. He hated everything that distorted God's objectives and turned them against the welfare of people. He was especially angry, therefore, with the "church." Up into the temple of God He went and drove out the buyers and sellers. "My house shall be known as a house of prayer. . . . And there were blind and lame men who came up to him in the temple, and he healed them there."[53] That is what the church is for, He seemed to say. "Woe unto you . . . you hypocrites that . . . have forgotten the weightier commandments of the law: justice, mercy and honor; you did ill to forget

---

[48]Jn. 5:16.
[49]Mt. 20:32.
[50]*God's Search for Man* (New York: Farrar, Strauss & Giroux, 1955), p. 369.
[51]Mk. 7:34.
[52]Rom. 8:23; 2 Cor. 5:2, 4.
[53]Mt. 21:12.

one duty while you performed the other.''[54] He almost flaunted His sabbath healings in the face of the Pharisees to awaken them to the priorities of the kingdom of God.

He loved.

He was moved to compassion. Practically the sum of the Christian message is found in the simple dialogue with the leper: "Lord, if you will, you can make me clean." "I will; be clean."[55] That will was the will of love. Love moves out of itself: "When he came ashore, he saw a great crowd; his heart went out to them, and he cured those of them who were sick."[56] Love is determined to help: "I will come and heal him (the centurion's servant)."[57] There was a profound intimacy in His love. It was not casual. "Lord, he whom thou lovest lies here sick. . . . He sighed heavily and was deeply moved . . . then Jesus wept."[58] There is hope in the universe. The sick are loved, and God weeps for man.

He loved widely, yet personally.

At times one almost gets a sense of mass healings. "Great multitudes went with them, and He healed them."[59] There was a reckless profligacy of healing power and love. At the same time, He was intensely personal. He wanted to get in touch with the individual, and sometimes that meant physical contact. "And Jesus, moved to compassion, touched their eyes."[60] Strikingly, "he reached out his hand and touched him (the leper)."[61] This dramatic act, a totally unusual thing in His tradition and environment, is full of implication. To everyone He was saying: "God's health is for you."

He healed relevantly.

Jesus kept cultural contact. He healed understandably. To touch a leper was not understandable. The new wine was breaking the old skin. Once the point was made, however, He stayed within the context. "Go, show yourself to the priest," he ordered the healed man.[62] Christ the Healer was within His situation. It is in that sense too that we must interpret the combination of physical touching and saliva.[63]

He crossed lines.

He healed inclusively. Of the Roman centurion whose servant He healed

[54]Mt. 23:23.
[55]Mt. 8:3.
[56]Mt. 14:14.
[57]Mt. 8:7.
[58]Jn. 11:3, 33-34.
[59]Mt. 19:2.
[60]Mt. 20:34.
[61]Mt. 8:3.
[62]Mt. 8:4.
[63]Mk. 7:34; 8:22-26.

at Capernaum, he said: "Many shall come from the east and the west, and will take their places in the kingdom of God."[64] He made the same point when He cast out the unclean spirit from the daughter of the Gentile woman: "Go home content."[65] In the full sense of the term, he was "the man for others." Is it not this that people outside the Christian fold have always noted and wondered? His extension of the principle was absolute: "Love your enemies . . . do good to those who hate you."[66]

He healed as a servant.

He healed without ostentation. Alongside His rejection of the raw use of power, He turned His back on acclaim. So often "he laid strict charge on them that they should not make him known."[67] He deliberately withdrew from the popular results of His healing activity. "Knowing then that they meant to come and carry him off so as to make a king of him, Jesus once again withdrew on a hillside alone."[68] He set the tone for all future healers when He pointed out that He had not come to have service done to Him; "He came to serve others and to give his life as a ransom for many."[69]

He was urgent.

He was urgent in His task. He had a sense of little time. In fact, He had only three years. (Do we have more?) He knew that the night was coming, and He must work while there is day. So He kept Himself available and worked to exhaustion levels. In that He was in touch with the secret of the universe. The secret is that God has exhausted Himself for us. "My Father has never yet ceased His work, and I am working too."[70]

The attitude of Christ the Healer is a many-splendoured thing of love.

3. See His Power

. . . See Him . . . See Him.

It is time to look directly at His power. You have witnessed the power of the Healer and believe it, I know. Yet see it again at this time as you plan your onslaught against evil. I will be reminding you of His struggle and suffering, but first see His authority that He shares with you along with His struggle.

The Spirit and power.

From the *human* aspect the power of Christ the Healer had a source outside of Himself. It was strongly related to His anointing by the Spirit of God and to prayer. Both of these are within the reach of the people of God.

At His baptism the Holy Spirit descended upon Jesus, and He returned

---

[64]Mt. 8:11.
[65]Mk. 7:29.
[66]Mt. 5:44.
[67]Mt. 12:16.
[68]Jn. 6:15.
[69]Mt. 20:28.
[70]Jn. 5:17.

from the Jordan "full of the Spirit." By the same Spirit He was led into the wilderness, and from there He came back into Galilee "with the power of the Spirit upon Him." Then as He declared His Messianic mission in the synagogue at Nazareth, He announced, "The Spirit of the Lord is upon me; He has anointed me." That Spirit was the source of His authority over demonic power and disease. In an important passage that I have quoted earlier, He declares: "But if, when I cast out devils, I do it through the Spirit of God, then it must be that the kingdom of God has already appeared among you."[71] St. Luke puts the same thought in slightly different words: "But if, when I cast out devils, I do it *through God's power*, then it must be that the kingdom of God has suddenly appeared among you."[72] Spirit and power go hand in hand for the Healer and for His followers.

Prayer and power.

The second source of His power was prayer. Prayer seems to have been the contact point and conduit for his grasping of the power of His Father. He felt the need for prayer, particularly in His task of healing. After the multitudes came to Him and He healed them of their infirmities, it is said that "he would steal away from them into a desert and pray there."[73] Prior to His dramatic, and everlastingly meaningful cry to Lazarus, "Come forth!", He had lifted up His eyes and said: "Father, I thank thee for hearing my prayer."[74]

At the same time as we recognize these elements viewed from the human side of Jesus' healing power, we must also recognize from the divine side a supra-rational power that is unique to Him. How shall we distinguish between these different levels of healing power represented by Christ, church, and world? Perhaps we may speak of a rational therapy that is the common gift of God to all human beings. Further, we may speak of a supra-rational therapy that is the extraordinary power resident in Christ, which He shared in a partial way with His first disciples. Finally, we may speak of Christian therapy that combines the best strengths of rational therapy together with the same resources of Spirit and power that Jesus possessed. These when joined and placed in the service of His Kingdom, under the blessing of the King, give to the healing ministry of Christ's people a special character, authority, and possibility.

The power unleashed.

In the mighty struggle against evil the power of the Healer was unleashed at two points: against sickness, as the result of evil; and against satan and sin, as the cause of evil. The effects of His healing power we know, and I shall not repeat those familiar episodes that demonstrated it so clearly. The Word of the Lord brought re-creative energy in a kind of Genesis II. "Who touched

[71]Mt. 12:28.
[72]Lu. 11:20.
[73]Lu. 6:12.
[74]Jn. 11:41.

me. . . . somebody touched me. . . . I can tell that power has gone out from me.''[75] There is breathless awe in the report: "Everyone who touched him was restored to health.''[76]

He also unleashed His power against sin and satan as the cause of evil. In Christ's day the Jews had inherited the view that there was a direct line leading from a specific sin to a specific punishment. If there was sickness, it indicated retribution for a sin. Jesus breaks through this rigid dogma,[77] but He nevertheless recognizes that sin is the fundamental evil. His ultimate concern is to liberate humanity, indeed all creation, from its shackles. "Look," says the Baptist, "This is the Lamb of God; this is he who takes away the sin of the world.''[78] It is the passage reporting the healing of the palsied man that illustrates the Healer's concern.

> Tell me which command is more lightly given, to say to a man, Thy sins are forgiven, or to say, rise up and walk? And now to convince you that the Son of Man has authority on earth to forgive sin while he is on earth (here he speaks to the palsied man), Rise, take up thy bed with thee, and go home. And he rose. . . .[79]

Some who are engaged in healing ministries may at times have felt a certain hesitation about the affirmation that Christ's core concern was the overcoming of sin. A kind of nervous tic has developed as a result of the bland assumption by some Christians that the healing of the sick is therefore a secondary concern. We need to be healed from this nervous reaction as much as others need to be healed from the disease of false comparisons between the preaching of the Gospel and the healing of the sick. I suppose that of all people healers will be the first to recognize the need to penetrate to and deal with root causes. Jesus came to deal with the root cause, leaving for us the ample task of proclaiming the good news that He has done so and ministering to its lingering effects in the agony of creation. In His last high priestly prayer the Healer prayed:[80]

> Father, the hour has come; glorify thy Son that the Son may glorify thee, since thou hast given him power over all mankind, to give eternal life to all whom thou hast given him.

In Him God as it were "travelled in His strength . . . mighty to save,''[81] and Christian healers join with all believers in the paean of praise for the One Who has broken the power of sin and removed the sting of death. "Thanks be to God!" all healers cry, and will yield to none in their devotion to the task of proclaiming His victory to the world.

---

[75]Lu. 7:45.
[76]Mt. 4:36.
[77]Lu. 13:1; Jn. 9:3; 11:4.
[78]Jn. 1:29.
[79]Mt. 9:5-6.
[80]Jn. 17:2.
[81]Is. 63:11.

Even dealing with sin, however, was not dealing with the final issue. Behind sin stands the Evil One, whom the Healer called the father of lies. Much has been written on the subject of demon possession as it expressed itself in Jesus' day, and consideration has been given to its possible relation to mental disorientation and disease. That is an unfinished exploration. Despite all natural explanations that may be adduced, however, we are faced with the overwhelming fact that the Healer regarded Himself as engaged in warfare with the Evil One and all his powers. Reading the events of Christ's encounter with the devil is like viewing a titanic struggle on a screen. The devil is strong indeed, but a stronger one has come, and He has entered his house and bound him up.[82] God's reign is declared, and the axe is laid to the root of evil's power. Evil recognizes that and recoils in fear.

> Why dost thou meddle with us, Jesus of Nazareth? Hast thou come to make
> an end of us? I recognize thee for what thou art, the Holy One of God. . . .
> Silence! Jesus said, Come out of him![83]

Like a cheerleader after a Steelers game, when the seventy disciples came back, rejoicing that the devils were subject to them, the Healer cries: "I watched while Satan was cast down like a lightning flash from heaven!"[84] We, in our turn, have watched and cheered in faith, as He rose from the dead, breaking the power of evil once and for all, ascended into heaven and took captivity captive. The mighty act of redemption is all but complete, as the Risen Lord prepares to come again.

The power of Christ the Healer is greater than the power of the devil. Do you identify with that?

But the warfare goes on, and now it is time to see the Healer broken for the world.

4. See His Suffering

See Him . . . See Him . . .

The devil bruised His heel, and the Healer is wounded. Christ the Healer suffered to heal. He is the prototype of all healers, who must suffer as they heal; who, in fact, must suffer in order to heal.

In His temptations.

Jesus suffered to heal. He suffered in His temptations. He was tempted like any other healers.

He was tempted both by His popularity and by His unpopularity. He was invited to yield to the siren call of popularity and prestige, and to take the credit due to God. Sometimes when the multitudes saw the dumb speaking, the lame walking, and the blind receiving their sight, "they praised the God of

---

[82]Mt. 12:29.
[83]Lu. 1:24.
[84]Lu. 10:18.

34

Israel."[85] That was the result that Jesus sought. Other times they wanted to exalt Him, for what Jesus regarded as the wrong reasons. The path of glory beckoned Him, as it has beckoned every healer, and resistance took spiritual effort. "Get thee behind me, Satan," He had to cry.

On the other hand, He was tested by His unpopularity, in that pendulum experience known to healers. He took on the cause of the ailing and the oppressed. That is not always a popular cause. "They entreated him to leave their country."[86] He was an activist healer, and that leads to danger. The power structures hounded him and sought his life. He wondered at that. "Why do you design to kill me?" he asked, after He had healed on the sabbath.[87] It was after He raised Lazarus from the dead that it is reported: "From that day forward, they plotted his death."[88] He had a feeling of depression and was tempted. "And now my soul is distressed. What am I to say? I will say, Father save me from undergoing this trial."[89]

In His loneliness.

Jesus suffered in His loneliness. Healers know the feeling. It is profound and enervating. Who understood what He was doing as He healed? No one had a clear sense of what it was all about. His own brothers grappled with Him and tried to drag Him home. His disciples attempted to dissuade Him from His insane course. Again and again, He had to chide those nearest to Him for their lack of understanding, not an easy thing to do. There is a remarkable little note in the Gospel of Luke that seems to illustrate the point. When Peter struck off the ear of Malchus, the high priest's servant, Luke reports that the Healer "touched his ear and healed him."[90] That information, however, is not found in any of the other Gospels, although they report the incident. Luke noticed, but he was a physician. Healers are lonely, and their true efforts and real sorrows are seldom known. Will we ever know how lonely the Healer was and what this meant to Him?

He suffered to heal.

Christ the Healer did not only suffer *as* He healed, however; He suffered in order *to* heal. That is, suffering is not an accidental component of healing, but it is a part of the function itself. His healing task could not be accomplished without His involvement in that which He was healing, and that meant suffering of profoundest measure. Can we follow Him along that road?

> We are going up to Jerusalem. . . . Have you the strength to drink the cup I am to drink of? They said, we have. And he told them, You shall indeed drink of my cup.[91]

---

[85]Mt. 15:31.
[86]Mt. 8:34.
[87]Jn. 7:20.
[88]Jn. 11:53.
[89]Jn. 12:27.
[90]Lu. 22:51.
[91]Mt. 20:18.

Part way they went along that road with Him, and part way you will go with Him, but not all the way. Now we are penetrating into the deepest mystery of God the Healer—He Himself bore our sorrows and our griefs.

One of the most important passages for the understanding of the ministry of Christ the Healer and our own healing ministry is Matthew 8, 16-17.

> And when evening came, they brought to him many persons who were possessed, and he cast out the evil spirits with his word, and he healed all that were sick, in fulfillment of the word spoken by Isaiah the Prophet: He took our infirmities upon himself and *bore our sicknesses.*

The words "He took our infirmities and bore our diseases" are a direct quotation of Isaiah's prophecy (53:4): "Surely, he has borne our griefs and carried our sorrows." That Old Testament passage, more literally translated, would read: "Surely, he has borne our pains and carried our afflictions." The Hebrew terms "pains" *(kholi)* and "afflictions" *(maccōv)* can be used to denote either physical suffering resulting from disease, or in a wider metaphoric sense, to denote the grief that results from calamities. In view of the total context of Isaiah 53 this passage is normally interpreted in the broader sense— the Suffering Servant is bearing the calamitous sorrow of sin.[92] Yet St. Matthew takes the passage in its narrower sense, viz., "He bore our *diseases.*" The intention is clearly to point to our physical sicknesses, for the prophecy is fulfilled by Jesus in the healing of the mother-in-law of St. Peter.

This remarkable shift of emphasis points minimally to the intimacy of the healing of soul and of body, the healing of sin and the healing of the consequences of sin. But certainly this thought has not exhausted the meaning. Two implications are possible. The first is that the Healer bore our physical sicknesses, but only in a manner of speaking; He bore them in the sense of bearing them away, penultimately by healing some of the ailing, ultimately by destroying sin itself. This meaning is preferred by commentators such as H.A.W. Meyer:[93]

> But when their ailments are taken away from the disease, the marvellous compassionate one who does this stands forth as he who carries them away, and, as it were, bears the burden lifted from the shoulder of others. The idea is plastic, poetical, and not to be understood as meaning an actual personal feeling of the diseases thus removed.

The second implication reflects the literal sense of the passage, that is, that the Suffering Servant actually bore our sicknesses. In some way in His ministry Jesus felt and bore the weight and sorrow of our illness, just as He felt and bore the weight and punishment of our sins. The text seems to indicate a real bearing and not a bearing away. To what extent shall we take this possible

---

[92]Following 1 Pet. 2:24, which, however, really refers to Is. 53:12: "Yet he bore the sin of many."

[93]*Critical and Exegetical Commentary on the New Testament,* tr. by P. Christie, Vol. I (Edinburgh: T. & T. Clark, 1877), p. 256.

implication seriously? Healing of any kind, physical or spiritual, is costly. (Who has ever said that it is easy to heal?) Christ the Healer was not a magician. When He takes away sin, He suffers for sin. When He takes away disease, in some way—and I leave with you and your own experience to decide in what way—He suffers that too. He is wounded to heal. He is totally wounded to totally heal. From that suffering there is no escaping: "They offered him a drink of wine, mixed with gall, which he tasted but would not drink."[94]

As we encourage Christians in parishes to become more involved in healing we are inviting them not to a theology of glory but to a theology of the cross. Those who have the vision of Christ the Healer and would follow His healing path, must participate in and really bear the sorrows of the wounded, even as they proclaim the victory of God. How shall they do this? One way is by sympathy, by suffering with (that is what *sym patheo* means). The other way is by dealing with their own wounds in such a way that they become a resource for others. As to the former, we know how wearing true sympathy can be; to feel with another person involves giving, the expenditure of energy, frequent stress, a participation in suffering. As to the latter, let me share with you the valuable thoughts of Henri Nouwen regarding the wounded healer:[95]

> Since it is his task to make visible the first vestiges of liberation for others, he must bind his own wounds carefully in anticipation of the moment when he will be needed. He is called to be the wounded healer, the one who must look after his own wounds, but at the same time be prepared to heal the wounds of others. He is both the wounded minister and the healing minister.

He goes on to suggest that as Jesus made His own broken body the way to health, to liberation and to new life, so must we.

> Like Jesus, he who proclaims liberation is called not only to care for his own wounds . . . but also to make his wounds into a major source of healing power.

Perhaps that is as close as we can come to the Healer in the bearing of the griefs of those we serve, and as Nouwen indicates, the ministries of such healers will be

> a witness to the living truth that the wound which causes us to suffer now, will be revealed to us later as the place where God intimated his new creation.

He healed in hope.

The path of the healing Christ goes through suffering to victory. The way of the kingdom is suffering love. The promise of the kingdom is that love conquers in the end. He suffered to heal, but the victory was always in sight for

---

[94]Mt. 27:34.
[95]*The Wounded Healer: Ministry in Contemporary Society* (New York: Image Books, 1979), pp. 82ff.

the Healer. Every healing confirmed for the Son of Man that the kingdom is coming. He did not and could not heal all the sick. He was content with partial victories, for He saw a vision too. His vision was the vision of God the Healer and His final victory. He saw a new heaven and a new earth, God's tabernacle pitched among humans, God wiping every tear from their eyes, with no more death or mourning or cries of distress or sorrow, God making all things new.[96] Sustained by the vision the Healer passed through His suffering and claimed the victory. To those who are still on the field of struggle He is the Sign of the Kingdom, and the signal He gives to us is: "Patience, I am coming soon."

That promise puts His victory in sight for us too. We are healing in the end time. We are healing in the shadow of the final victory. The Healer has taken His power and reigns. The suffering is bearable, our partial victories are sufficient signs, and our hope is alive. Our one overriding concern is to be faithful to Him. "Blessed is that servant who is found doing when his Lord comes."[97]

5. The Community of Faith and Love

We are the doers.

Until He comes we represent Him and continue His healing ministry in a suffering world. We, the community of faith and love, are His healing body walking through Jerusalem, Samaria, and the uttermost parts of the world.

Christ's healing body is a community of faith. Faith surrounds the ministry of Christ the Healer. It appears both as a pre-condition and as a consequence of His healing. Sometimes it is the faith of the sick person that is involved. To the blind man He said, "Do you believe that I am able to do this?"[98] Often it was the faith of the family that was the critical factor. To Jairus He declared: "Thou hast only to believe."[99] To the father of the demon-possessed son the Healer announced, "If thou canst believe, to him who believes everything is possible." Whereupon the father cried aloud, "Lord, I believe, succour thou my unbelief."[100] Sometimes it was a friend or friends who had the faith. Looking up at the bearers of the sick man as they suddenly appeared in the breach of the ceiling, Jesus "seeing their faith" cured the palsied man.[101] To those who shared His work of healing Jesus gave the call to faith:[102]

> Why was it that we could not cast it out? . . . Because you had no faith. . . .
> There is no way of casting out such spirits as these except by prayer and fasting.

---

[96]Rev. 22:4-5. While this is St. John's vision, it provides an essential summary of what is intimated in the eschatological passages of the Gospels. Again and again Jesus refers to His "going to the Father." He looks forward to the time when He will drink with us of the fruit of the vine "in the kingdom of my Father" (Mt. 26:29).

[97]Mt. 24:45.

[98]Mt. 9:28; cf. Mt. 15:28.

[99]Mt. 5:36.

[100]Mk. 9:23.

[101]Mt. 9:2.

[102]Mt. 17:17ff.

Faith is involved in both the receiving and the giving of healing. That means nothing less than that the community of faith, the Christian congregation, is poised to carry on healing ministry both within the body of believers and at the same time to be a healing body for those around them. As it prepares to follow the Healer on His mission, such a congregation will plead: "Lord, succour our faith!"

His healing body is a community of love. As faith surrounds the ministry of the Healer, selfless love provides its motif and heart. Faith placed in God the Healer works by love. The body of believers is now the loving, healing Christ in the world. The Lord of Healing Who "purchased and won us . . . with His holy precious blood and His innocent suffering and death" did so that we might be His own and serve Him and His world as He served it. The Leader says to His followers: "Continue ye in my love." In so continuing the community of love sees the world as Christ saw it and responds accordingly. Beyond that, it sees Christ Himself in the world it serves, and in serving the world therefore serves and loves the Lord Himself. When the Healer comes again in His Kingdom of glory, He shall say to His community of love:[103]

> I was hungry, and you gave me food, thirsty, and you gave me drink; I was a stranger and you brought me home, naked, and you clothed me, sick and you cared for me, a prisoner, and you came to me. . . . When was it that we saw thee sick. . . . And the King will answer them, Believe me, when you did it to one of the least of my brethren here, you did it for me.

Thus we bind up the wounds of the Healer Who was wounded for us.

The Christian congregation, the assembly of those called out to follow Jesus Christ, is then a community of faith and love. A community of faith and love is a healing community. It is a sign of the kingdom of God. How shall the members of the community of faith and love become what they are? How shall such a healing community organize itself to take up the healing task of its Lord with new and creative energy? How can we help? There are certainly many practical things to be done. I am convinced, however, that in the end there is only one possible starting-point for us all, and that is a fresh involvement with Jesus Christ. I have therefore tried to put the vision of Christ the Healer before your eyes. It may not be a comfortable vision. Dietrich Bonhoeffer put it well when he said:[104]

> All the activity of the disciples is subject to the clear precepts of their Lord. They are not left free to choose their own methods or adopt their own conception of the task. Their work is to be Christ-work, and therefore they are absolutely dependent on the will of Jesus. Happy are they whose duty is fixed by such precept and who are therefore free from the tyranny of their own ideas and calculations. . . . The proclamation and activity of the messengers are identical with that of Christ himself.

It may not be the comfortable vision, but it is the inspiring one, the one vision

---

[103]Mt. 25:35ff.
[104]*The Cost of Discipleship* (London: SCM Press, 1959), pp. 184f.

that will lift us up and out of our comfortable pews, the only one that will set the church on fire for God. He is both the Pattern and the Power. That is why St. Paul affirmed: "May all the wealth of Christ's inspiration have its shrine among you!"[105]

See Him . . . See Him . . .

See Him with His hand outstretched over the doubting and faltering people of God. "Eirene-Shalom-Peace be upon you! Even as the Father sent me, so send I you!" As His final gift of grace to those whom He sends to be the members of the broken world, He who was and is and is to come declares:

> I will come to you. . . . He who has my commandments and keeps them, he it is who loves me, and he who loves me will be loved by my Father, and I will love him and manifest myself to him.[106]

The healer has not gone. He is with us on the plain. To every Healer who heals for him, He says, I love you and I will meet you on the way.

I close in the Name of Christ the Healer, and leave you with a strong word and a word of hope.

The strong word is a word from the Lord: "How is it that you call me Master! Master!, and will not do what I bid you?"

And now the words of witness and hope:

"The centurion said, Come down before my child dies!"

"Go back home, thy son is to live."

"And the man began his journey home, putting his trust in the words that Jesus had spoken to him."

---

[105]Col. 3:16.
[106]Jn. 14:18, 21.

Rev. Donald H. Larsen

CHAPTER III

Health and Healing in the Lutheran Church: Tradition and Practice

by Donald H. Larsen
in collaboration with
David E. Farley and Norman E. Minich

TRADITION: A SIMPLE LINE

The tradition for most Lutheran congregations in the United States in regard to health and healing follows a simple line. It was the duty of the state to provide welfare and health care. If an occasional individual succeeded in founding a private agency for health and healing, it might receive support, most often at arm's length. Only in recent years have Lutheran congregations in any significant numbers become involved directly in the search for the practice of health and prevention of illness as Christian communities.

Had Lutheran congregations followed the words rather than the actions of Martin Luther, the result might have been different. Though Luther stressed justification by faith alone, he understood its sterility without acts of love and mercy. For Luther, the "neighbor" was the target of faith active in love. "Do you want to serve Christ?" he asked on one occasion; "Then go to your neighbor who is sick. There you will find Christ."

Despite such concern for what we today would quickly recognize as "social ministry," Luther found it politically inevitable that he would turn the role of the church over to the princes. This relieved the congregations of their obligations to help the needy. No longer were Christians, *in the name of the church*, to wear what Luther had called "the 'red dress' of welfare work over the white undergarment of faith." That red garment was now the uniform of *Christians and others, in the name of the state*.

State institutionalism of welfare became dominant in the lands of early Lutheranism. It was August Hermann Francke's work at Halle which seems to have partially altered the tradition.

Martin Scharlemann, in a 1958 paper, "The Theological and Historical Basis for Lutheran Welfare," describes Francke's method as being of special interest to people in the U.S. He said, "It inaugurated a new epoch and provides major features of the pattern of our own beginnings here in America.

They were: 1) The impetus for welfare work must come from an individual or an agency within the church, rather than from the church itself, as an organized association; 2) consecration can compensate for lack of competence. Both of these accents are inherent in the pietist view of the church. *We are affected by this theology as much in our view of welfare responsibilities as we were in other respects.*"[1]

Theodore G. Tappert, in *Christian Social Responsibility: The Lutheran Heritage,* wrote: "Although not the first of their kind, the institutions of mercy which Francke established in Halle made a tremendous impression on contemporaries and may be taken as the most imposing monument to the social concern of the Lutheran pietists."[2]

So, for Lutherans in the United States, the personally initiated institutional pattern seemed the only answer. When someone had agonized long enough, a small hospital, an orphanage, a home for the aged was founded. That was true for Sister Elizabeth Feti, for what is now Lutheran Medical Center, Brooklyn, N.Y., and also for Pastor Henry Muhlenberg, the founder of the German Benevolence Society in 1764. The GBS was primarily to help immigrants, but Muhlenberg's health interest led him to keep a chest of herb remedies just inside the church door.

Health services have come a long way since the herb-chest. In 1849, William Passavant opened the Pittsburgh Infirmary, said to be the first American Protestant Hospital Association. He later founded hospitals in Chicago, Milwaukee, and elsewhere.

Of J. F. Buenger, the founder of the first Protestant Hospital west of Pittsburgh, Martin Scharlemann wrote, "He had always wanted to build a hospital, but he met with great difficulties. Due to his personal persistence the hospital association was founded in December, 1858. He himself was elected as president and continued in that capacity until his death in 1882."[3]

TRADITION: THE INNER MISSION

Just as Passavant was individually opening the first hospitals in America, the day for the full unfolding of the Inner Mission came as a result of the 1848 revolution across Europe. Johann Hinrich Wichern (1808-81), at a special *Kirchentag* of church leaders at Wittenberg, in September, 1848, appeared to be a prophet. He called the church to *love* as its responsibility as well as *faith.* Wichern saw power and promise in a revised priesthood of all believers, "wherein men and women could share in the desperately needed *inner mission* of the church."[4]

---

[1]Martin H. Scharlemann, "The Theological and Historical Basis for Lutheran Welfare," Department of Social Welfare, St. Louis, Mo., 1958, p. 35. (Emphasis added.)
[2]Harold C. Letts, Editor, *Christian Social Responsibility, Volume Two, The Lutheran Heritage,* Muhlenberg Press, Philadelphia, 1957, Chapter 2, "Orthodoxy, Pietism, and Rationalism" by Theodore G. Tappert, p. 73.
[3]Scharlemann, p. 36.
[4]Letts, Chapter 3, "The Church and the Rise of Modern Society," by E. Theodore Bachmann, p. 102.

Never ordained, Wichern remained a theological candidate. He grasped the possibilities of voluntary societies, used lay workers for his training center for delinquent boys, stressed lay activity in Christ's name on the basis of the priesthood of all believers. The Inner Mission would become a force, a kind of Christian socialism, to defeat the specter of state communism. His blind spot was his emphasis on love at the expense of justice.

As Wichern trained deacons, Theodore Fliedner (1800-67) trained deaconesses. At Kaiserswerth-on-the-Rhine, training and service were begun which, in time, recruited thousands of women, primarily as nurses, and met contemporary needs. Some of Fliedner's deaconess-nurses served in Passavant's hospitals in the U.S.

Wilhelm Loehe (1808-72) and his U.S. followers, more than others, "gave the Inner Mission a churchly orientation. . . . If Loehe was somewhat of a romanticist as well as a stimulating theologian, later generations are indebted to this village pastor (in Bavaria's Neuendettelsau) for seeing beyond his crossroads and for linking social responsibility to a Lutheran church, which he, earlier than others, beheld as a world-wide fellowship with a global task."[5]

In Denmark and Norway, after 1850, the Inner Mission came to mean evangelism. Charitable institutions and social reform were not as important as the main task of reaching the growing numbers of those neglected by the preaching of the church, especially in the cities. In Sweden, the *laesare*, Bible-reading and upright laymen, were leading a "second reformation."[6]

THE TRADITION: HOME MISSION

The voluntary character of the Inner Mission in Europe made it almost completely adaptable to American conditions. "From the outset, Passavant differentiated between home missions and inner missions. 'Home' missions meant the task of providing churches for native and new Americans; 'inner' missions meant the intensification of life within the church. This involved evangelism, worship, stewardship, polity, discipline, education, plus the relief of the sick, the poor, and the neglected."[7]

American voluntarism, combined with the political desire for religious separation, soon disrupted that neat balance.

Frederick Conrad Wynecken (1810-1876), immigrant frontier pastor first in Baltimore, then in Indiana, saw what was happening to the Germans in America and their Lutheran faith. His *Notruf* (1840) was a stirring appeal to Wichern, Loehe, and others. Help came. So did the sticky "foreign" label.

Almost as Wyncken became known as the father of "home" missions, it appeared the die was cast. The tradition would become *Home Missions* first, and, if you could get around to it, *Inner Missions*, too. Small wonder that, with this early set, most charitable work was begun and carried on by individuals, rather than by the churches as such.

[5]*Ibid.*, p. 109.
[6]*Ibid.*, p 110.
[7]*Ibid.*, p. 111.

Neither the term "health-care" nor "health and healing" is a part of the Lutheran tradition in social mission beyond hospitals until very recently. After the Civil War the Lutheran church was challenged to adapt to the ways of the American society. Its "foreign" label was offering to come unglued.

American Protestantism after 1865 evolved into two major types: one was pietistic, traditional, and individual; the other was critical, contemporary, and social. There was not always a distinct separation between the two, and while both often believed in progress, the individually-minded tended eventually toward fundamentalism and the socially-minded toward liberalism. Most Lutherans tended toward the individual type.

The General Synod seems to have been one exception. It was confessionally moderate and socially conservative. Its members participated in charity, supported benevolence, helped immigrants and new settlers, and fought specific social evils. At the same time they supported temperance and the sabbath observance, and this sometimes appeared puritanical to other Lutherans. It did leave room for preventive as well as remedial action in community life. As E. Theodore Bachmann puts it, even "they viewed social problems hopefully, but at a grand theological distance . . . its participation in the social gospel movement was more talk than action."[8]

"Theses on the Inner Mission," drawn up in 1905, and adopted by the General Council, were expanded by Jeremiah Franklin Ohl into a widely used book, The Inner Mission, in 1911. "By 1914 the accent was clearly on churchwise education for Christian service in the manner of an evangelizing and institutional Inner Mission. Silent as to social justice, and far short of matching the scope of the social gospel, the Americanized Inner Mission nevertheless exposed something of the social potential in a justifying faith become active in love."[9]

Among those who rose to the challenge of advocating social Christianity were Joseph Cook and Washington Gladden. John H. W. Stukenburg (1835-1903), professor at Wittenberg College and Seminary, gave an interpretation of "Social Evils" in his Christian Sociology of 1880. He urged the church to meet social issues and not leave them to non-Christian forces. In none of these writings is there more than a minor emphasis on health and healing.

This same stress on evangelical faith, at work in other parts of the world, leads Bachmann to write three small paragraphs which may be the most prophetic of his summary. He subtitled it: "Overseas Missions and the Creation of a New Society." It is worth a complete citation here:

> The oneness of missions at home and abroad was impressed upon many a churchman in the "great century." The primary task of European societies, temporarily sending home mission pastors to America, was to prepare foreign missionaries for Africa, Asia, and the Pacific islands. Ever since Ziegenbalg in eighteenth-century India or Muhlenberg in colonial

[8]Ibid., pp. 131-132.
[9]Ibid., p. 134.

46

America cherished hopes of setting up miniatures of the multiform charities they had known at Halle, Lutheran missions joined social responsibility to spiritual purpose. Indeed, like Christian missions over the centuries, the preaching of the good news of God's redeeming love in Jesus Christ has sought a new community.

Large or small, the new communities springing up in non-Christian cultures revealed afresh the claim of God upon the whole life of individuals and society. In the simple sequences of missionary endeavor, like that of a Heyer in India, the great redemption could be suggested in such matters as the missionary's identification with his people, his painstaking learning of their language, his translation and communication of the Word in their words, his attempts to transform the old and to implant the new. His preaching and teaching as well as his healing and helping ministry grew into chapels, churches, schools, colleges, clinics, hospitals, and homes. In crafts and fields and business, in the common life as well, a new ethic and practice of stewardship grew out of the Christian calling and understanding of vocation. A native ministry and lay participation in the tasks of spreading the gospel brought family and economic life, culture, and religion under the judgment of divine Law; and released the penitent for new life in the gospel.

What was thus happening among Telugus, Zulus, or Bataks, disclosed the social responsibility inherent in the spiritual ministry of evangelical faith. To be sure, these were small beginnings. Under the weight of frustration, they often failed to shine with the light of their ultimate hope. But there was something in this for the "sending churches" in Europe and America. A lengthening perspective discloses that God may have been using the young Christians in distant fields to prepare a message whose full import is only now becoming apparent for a secularized Christendom.[10]

THE TRADITION: MOLDED BY AMERICA

At a July 1966 Workshop on the Church and Social Welfare, Martin E. Marty presented two lectures on theology and social welfare called "The Bearing of Social Welfare on Theology and the Church," and "The Bearing of Theology and Church on Social Welfare." In them Marty draws the setting for the church and outlines what he is sure would be continuing problems. They seem to have continued to this day.

First, the multi-faceted setting:

> If we view the subsequent history of welfare in the setting of Christendom we can avoid some problems. When the church takes on the whole burden of society, then all social welfare is an expression of the life of the church. Again no problem. But Christendom is disintegrating. The vast majority of social welfare workers and almost all social welfare funds are "public" and not gathered through Christian channels. Then comes the rejoinder: in that case, we are closer to early Christianity, pre-Christendom. Then, as now, the little flock of Christ was a wandering minority in a world of principalities and power. This, too, will not work because now Christendom has happened and the secular world has a different agenda and attitude after this event than it did when New Testament documents were written concerning untried Christianity in the Roman Empire.
>
> What has happened to change the setting in social welfare in our time— we have seen the breakup of the "ontocratic" world (F. A. van Leeuwen) in which communities had a grasp of reality against the background of an inclusive order of correspondence between eternal and temporal, infinite and finite, divine and human. This divine order was "merged" with history,

---

[10]*Ibid.*, pp. 134-135.

nature, society and especially of the state and all of society's patterns and structures were regarded, somehow, sacrally. Modern secular pluralistic society has seen the breakup of this view. Modern political constitutions are metaphysically silent and free societies tolerate a variety of views. Thus social welfare is undertaken today jointly by people who repudiate the Lordship of Christ, and by those who neglect to acknowledge it and by those who consciously are motivated by it.

Second the industrial revolution has occurred and has been so stepped up in our technological, industrialized and affluent society that social welfare has become more complex and specialized. Person to person relationships have changed, people are mobile. Economics dictate residence; experts handle cases. Words from the pulpit which imply that fulfilled regard for the neighbor can be carried out in the interpersonal and privatistic spheres are mere words, are hollow and beside the point. Christians today, if they want to take seriously the mandates of the message of God, know they have to work with and through the state, secular agencies, voluntary pluralistically-based organizations, and Christian units.[11]

Marty saw American social work, with its different hope than that of the whole Christian Gospel, as complementary to the Christian message. But he also saw it in need of constant judgment and redemption from a Lutheran church learning how to practice just the right amount of what Paul Tillich had called "withdrawal from history."

Marty's list of "eight problems for Lutherans" sounds unchanged a decade and a half later.[12] He did judge none of them incapable of redress, since most were "based on bad history, accidental relationships, or tendencies, and not integral to the definition or practice of social welfare work or Christian response."[13]

G. S. Thompson, at the same 1966 workshop, analyzes the differences in American Lutheran ecclesiology, church structures, and congregational approaches in an attempt to account for the widely proliferated response to social need represented by over 300 social service agencies, homes, and institutions then in existence.[14] One searches in vain for any emphasis on health and healing in the church other than a general call to "minister his love to the sick."

Indeed, it took the threat as seen in the rise of the "faith healing" phenomenon of the late 1950's and early 1960's in the U.S. to call forth a couple of statements. A "Report on Anointing and Healing" was adopted at the last convention of the United Lutheran Church in America in 1962, and "Christian Faith and the Ministry of Healing" was prepared as a statement of the Church Council of The American Lutheran Church and was approved for circulation to its congregations in July, 1965. The latter document looks at definitions of health and healing, the witness of scripture, and the theology of healing. It

[11]Martin E. Marty, "Two Lectures on Theology and Social Welfare," 1966. Mimeographed Paper, pp. 8-9.

[12]*Ibid.*, pp. 13-14.

[13]*Ibid.*, p. 15.

[14]G. S. Thompson, "The Role of Christianity in Church-Related Social Services," 1966. Mimeographed Paper.

states, "Healing is an expression of God's saving love for man. . . . Healing is not the only, nor even the primary, facet of the compassionate love of God. . . . It is necessary to keep clearly in mind the Biblical concept of the wholeness of man; the ministry of healing must be concerned with the total need of man. . . . The power to heal is from God alone. . . . The ministry of healing must be understood as an integral part of the coming of the kingdom of God through the total ministry of Jesus Christ, in whose ministry healing and preaching were closely associated. . . . The experience of healing is closely associated with faith. . . . Spiritual or faith healing of the sick . . . does not in any way disparage nor supplant the healing ministry as practiced by physicians, surgeons, nurses and others."[15]

The paper then gently recommends a three-way ministry of healing: congregational spiritual ministry through Word and prayer, a thankful use of physicians and the founding of hospitals and other institutions for the care and healing of the sick, and carefully controlled faith-healing services, for which seven rubrics were suggested, all cautiously and guardedly.

THE PRACTICE: CLINICAL EDUCATION AND PASTORAL COUNSELING

Its practitioners date the cry for clinically trained chaplains to about the turn of the present century. My colleague, David Farley, writes, in a memo to me for this paper, "In the early 1900's, as medical education began to change and become more clinical, the climate for clinical pastoral education training for chaplains improved. The early efforts in clinical training were divergent, geographically as well as philosophically and theologically. As the clinical pastoral education movement continued its development, the Lutheran church became involved at an early stage. Individual Lutherans were present and involved in the early meetings of all segments of the CPE activity. They included:

1. The Council for Clinical Training, formed in Boston in 1930.
2. The Institute of Pastoral Care, formed in 1944 from the New England Group, the Cabot Club, and the New England Theological Schools Committee on Clinical Training.
3. The Southern Baptist Association for CPE, formed in 1957.

"These three and the Lutheran Advisory Council of 1950 formed in 1967 the Association for Clinical Pastoral Education. Lutherans were full participants in the first National Conference on Clinical Training and Theological Education, June 6-7, 1944."

E. Thodore Bachmann was at that 1944 conference and, in a report to the National Lutheran Council observed that "Lutheran students, teachers and administrators would do well to acquire the skills and relate them to the theological content of the Lutheran heritage." He warned that "Clinical work as supervised training is not a cure-all for the problems of theological education.

---

[15]"Christian Faith and the Ministry of Healing," ALC, 1965, pp. 6-9.

49

It would therefore be most unfortunate if the Lutheran Church which over the centuries has been strong on 'seelsorge' would fail to take advantage of the opportunities offered by a program in clinical training. In America our church, though furnished by an unusual percentage of faithful pastors, has failed to see or appropriate many of the newer implications of pastoral care. As a church we have produced no 'Pastoralia' of our own. We have relied on translations and modifications of European works as well as non-Lutheran American books.'' Urging fuller fusion of faith and life by adding clinical to theological training, Bachmann warned, ''If we delay, then in an hour of global tragedy and personal frustration we shall be failing our fellowmen.'' He called for a Lutheran program of clinical training.[16]

Granger Westberg, Fredric Norstad, Henry Cassler, Carl Plack, A. R. Wentz, Gould Wickey, Edward Mahnke, Clarence Krumbholz, Henry Wind— these are the names most mentioned as the organizers of the Lutheran Advisory Council on Pastoral Care. It saw and carried out its work in two main areas. First, it encouraged seminaries to provide adequate training for students and continuing education for pastors, particularly for institutional ministries in state and Lutheran hospitals, prisons, and other settings. Most of those serving as institutional chaplains were looking for ways to improve that ministry and for further training in the field.

The second area was to set up accrediting procedures and to prepare and maintain a roster of qualified Lutheran supervisors in centers which could be used by the seminaries. At about the same time, chaplains were meeting with their denominational groups at the American Protestant Hospital Association. The Lutheran Hospital Association had been formed and chaplains and hospital administrators in Lutheran hospitals and welfare agencies were discussing training programs. Standards of the APHA chaplains' section called for a minimum of three years of pastoral experience in the parish ministry and at least 960 hours of clinical training for accreditation.

Of some of the missteps in those early years Fredric Norstad writes in a paper titled, ''Clinical Pastoral Education in the Lutheran Church,'' ''One of the deficiencies that some of us regret in theological education is the inadequacy of attention given to the doctrine of man, particularly to the nature of man and to the dynamics of his personality. While Christology must always occupy the central position in our theology, we question whether this doctrine is adequately understood without a better understanding of the human being. Just as with the individual, there must first come an awareness with himself before he feels a need of Christ. It is important to have a real understanding of the man for whom Christ died if full significance is to be realized.''[17]

By 1959, 26 Lutheran centers had been accredited in CPE and 145 Luther-

---

[16]E. Theodore Bachman, quoted at length in a mimeographed paper, ''The Lutheran Church and Clinical Pastoral Education,'' by Daniel H. Sandstedt, p. 4.

[17]Fredric Norstad, ''Clinical Pastoral Education in the Lutheran Church,'' Archives, Lutheran Council in the U.S.A., New York, 1956, p. 3.

an students were in training. In 1961 a permanent committee on Clinical Pastoral Education was authorized, and a full time staff position in the area of CPE was established. Henry Cassler assumed that post with the National Lutheran Council in 1962, and began the work of developing more adequate accreditation procedures regionally. He continued, with Walter Baepler, to lead the Department of Specialized Pastoral Care and Clinical Education in the Lutheran Council in the U.S.A. until his retirement.

Lutherans have thus been influential in the CPE movement almost since its beginning. Although CPE is involved in areas other than relating to those who are ill, healing in many forms has been a dominant part of their commitment. The trained chaplain and the establishment of departments of pastoral care were, and continue to be, involved in the beginnings of holistic and ecological approaches to health care. Currently there are over 600 full-time Lutheran chaplains related to the healing and health ministry.

In addition, there are approximately 150 Lutheran Pastoral Counselors. Pastoral counseling has become in the 60's and 70's a growing contribution to the healing process. Pastoral Counselors presently serve on the staff at the Lutheran General Hospital in Chicago, at multiservice agencies such as Lutheran Social Services of Minnesota, and in community counseling centers.

In 1976 the Division of Theological Studies, upon request of the general secretary of the Lutheran Council in the U.S.A., initiated a study dealing with the theological implications of the state supervision, regulation, and financing of ordained Lutheran pastors in ministries not directly related to the parish. As this study progressed, the division came to realize the appropriateness of a broader study of the issue of the relationship of pastoral counseling to the ordained ministry. The division's standing committee was aware of the work in this area that was in process within the church bodies participating in the Lutheran Council, but it also recognized the need for clarification and definition in regard to pastoral counseling and the ordained ministry and to the church-state relations raised by such non-parish ministries. It saw the potential value of an inter-Lutheran approach which would not contradict but enhance the study going on within the churches.

Therefore, in October 1976 the standing committee of the division requested the executive committee of the Lutheran Council to approve this broader study of the theological issues which pertain to the relationship between the ordained ministry and pastoral counseling as a specialized ministry. Both in November 1976 and May 1977 the executive committee affirmed the study. The understanding was that the basic document used would be, "The Ministry of the Church: A Lutheran Understanding," which had been adopted by the division's standing committee in March 1974.

Out of that study a "Statement on the Relationship of the Ordained Ministry to Pastoral Counseling" was developed and approved in March 1978 by the standing committees of the Division of Theological Studies and the Department of Specialized Pastoral Care and Clinical Education of the Lutheran Council in the U.S.A. as a contribution to the study and practice of pastoral counseling within the church bodies participating in the council.

Its definition of pastoral counseling is a first attempt among Protestants to give form to this growing discipline: "Theologically stated, Lutherans understand that pastoral counseling, as a specialized ministry of the church, is a therapeutic process in which Word and sacraments are operative. It is a ministry related to the gathered fellowship, carried on by ordained ministers who are specially equipped for it, who are called to it by the church, and who are accountable to the church and to appropriate professional peers. The aim of the entire process is that both counselor and counselee grow in grace, in self-acceptance, and in love of God and neighbor."[18]

TRADITION AND PRACTICE: HUMAN ECOLOGY

Probably no other movement, except that of the (w)holistic health centers, reported on at length in the paper by Granger Westberg, has had as much contribution to make toward molding the tradition and changing the practice than Fredric Norstad's Lutheran Institute of Human Ecology.

It is best to let "Fritz" tell his own story as briefly as possible:

> The Lutheran Institute of Human Ecology has evolved out of questions arising regarding the role of the church as it relates to health care in the 20th century. Specifically and historically, it came about when a church-related hospital, Lutheran Deaconess Hospital in Chicago's inner city, was confronted with the opportunity to build a new, modern institution. The decision to relocate and build was precipitated by circumstances which included a substantial overbedding at the old location and the spiraling costs of hospital operation which rendered economically unfeasible institutions of less than 400-bed capacity.
>
> Once a decision was made to build a modern hospital of larger size, some people involved began to ask very basic questions. Perhaps the most perplexing of all was the question of the legitimacy of the church's involvement in health care at this point in history. There could be little question about the propriety of church hospitals in the past. The majority of private hospitals in the U.S. had come into existence because hospitals were needed and the church had both the necessary concern for the sick and the organizational structure within which such institutions could be developed.
>
> However, by the mid-20th century, drastic changes had taken place, and we had in effect a brand new ball game. On the one hand the nation had become far more health conscious than in the past. The dramatic developments within medicine and science had led to a national preoccupation with health and a desire on the part of communities to make immediately available the miracles of modern medicine. Implementing this preoccupation and this desire was federal legislation occurring at the end of World War II providing through federal grants, for instance, the Hill-Burton Act of 1946, to make it possible for any community which needed hospital facilities to have them.
>
> It would be possible to take the position that the salt, light and leaven of the Gospel had influenced the social institution of government in such a way as to make unnecessary the church's involvement in health care. If the justification for such involvement was primarily that of providing otherwise absent facilities, people involved in the development and operation of Lu-

---

[18]"A Statement on the Relationship of the Ordained Ministry to Pastoral Counseling," *LCUSA*, 1978.

theran General and Deaconess Hospitals began to ask, however belatedly, whether it was appropriate for the church to build and operate hospitals.

Some who questioned such activity on the part of the church raised their questions out of what they felt was an inadequate demonstration of any significant and substantial difference between church hospitals and institutions operated under the aegis of non-ecclesiastical organizations.

The answer to this basic question was drawn from three roots. Chronologically, at least, the first answer came out of what is usually considered as secular sources. Medicine, largely influenced by psychiatry, was, in theory at least, committed to a new anthropology. The old Cartesian view of man was giving way to a recognition of the interrelationship of the many facets of the total person. During the 1950's we began to hear more and more about comprehensive medicine. While this term meant many things to many people, it was at least a partial redefinition of man and a step toward an interdisciplinary approach to his health care. In important support of such developments were the strengthening and growth of medical and psychiatric social work and clinical pastoral education.

This brings us to the second root, from which the answer was drawn: a new, or at least drastically modified, doctrinal anthropology within many segments of the Christian church. This development within theology is indeed interesting. I would like to be able to say that it grew out of the new Biblical studies and proceeded logically into modification of doctrine. However, I think this is untrue. I think the development was more intuitive than logical. As pastors and others became more and more concerned about this newly defined man and saw him in terms of his indivisibility and the dynamic interrelationship of the aspects of his being, it was simply assumed that the Gospel had relevance to the total human being.

This is not to say that the new Biblical studies were unimportant. Quite the contrary. The new Biblical studies had revealed certain substantial errors and pointed out their correction. Words that had previously been filtered through and modified by Greek and Cartesian thought had presented, to say the least, an ambiguous view of man and a considerable distortion of doctrine. But that which may have been arrived at intuitively now found support in a more accurate understanding of Biblical terms and a resultant clarity in exegesis.

The third root from which the answer was drawn is a more recent one and closely related to the foregoing. In the early 1960's, concomitant with the emergence of the indigenous churches in the developing nations, urgent questions were arising in the area of medical missions. To the indigenous churches moving toward independence and autonomy, the hospitals represented fantastic and disproportionate responsibilities and expense. Out of the urgency of this problem more and more people raised questions regarding the relationship between health and salvation. This was really the origin of the now historic Tuebingen I consultation. That consultation simply opened the door to further investigation. In a hundred different ways at a hundred different places, the consideration has continued. The Coonoor conference of March 1967 and the second Tuebingen consultation in September 1967 represent important steps toward eventual clarification of the issue. There is little doubt at this point that the church will ultimately accept the fact of an essential relationship between health and salvation. While forms, structure, and implementation will be debated for decades to come, there would seem to be little doubt about the eventual position of the church in this matter.[19]

---

[19]Fredric M. Norstad, "The Lutheran Institute of Human Ecology," *Lutheran Social Welfare*, Vol. 9, Spring, 1969, pp. 36-38.

THE TRADITION IS CHANGED BY: MEDICAL MISSIONS

Fritz Norstad's glowing endorsement of the Coonoor and Tuebingen conferences leads us to a brief presentation of the reverse influence of the Medical Mission programs of the Lutheran churches in recent years. Keep in mind as well the earlier statement by Bachmann on overseas missions and the creation of a new society.

The Tuebingen Consultation, and its counterparts held in Africa and North America, were jointly sponsored by the World Council of Churches and the Lutheran World Federation in 1967. Earlier in the same year a conference supported by the Wheat Ridge Foundation and the Lutheran Church-Missouri Synod through its Medical Missions Council was held in Coonoor, India.

The findings and affirmations are very similar and complementary. Each turned back to the sending churches the call to "understand itself as a healing community."[20] Each called for renewal in the understanding of that term. Each redefined "healing in the Christian understanding as the restoration of a dynamic harmony between God and man within man himself, and in man's relationship with his fellow men."[21]

The Coonoor conference's most notable theme was that of the unitary nature of all the things under consideration, linking illness and sin, health and salvation, body and spirit, ministry of Word and ministry of medicine.

The Tuebingen team, especially at the African conference, called for changes in the healing ministry of the church—not just new understandings but changes in practice. It asked that the church recognize that healing occurs within the normal work and fellowship, and that it see its services of public worship and the administration of the Sacraments as an essential part of the healing ministry. It requested healing services in home, church, or hospital, and close cooperation between the churches and all healing agencies.

In "The City of the Third World" of February, 1976, building on these international conferences and the inability of the Lutheran Council in the U.S.A. to launch its Department of Medical Missions, E. J. Holman examined North American Lutheran responses to world health needs. He called for a single, inter-Lutheran health ministries function within Lutheran World Relief, funded by the churches, and membership in the Christian Medical Commission.[22]

TRADITION AND PRACTICE: AND NOW, THE CONGREGATION

All of these thrusts have left the finger pointing at the untapped resource and change agents: the local congregations of the Lutheran churches. It remains for experts to assess the depth of the neo-pentecostal revival in American Lutheran congregations. More traditional sources of assistance seem to be

[20]Thomas A. Droege, "The Coonoor Conference," *Lutheran Social Welfare,* Volume 8, Spring 1968, No. 1, p. 40.
[21]Report of "Umpumolo Consultation on the Healing Ministry of the Church," *Lutheran Social Welfare*, Vol. 8, Winter 1968, No. 4, p. 55.
[22]E. J. Holman, "The Cry of the Third World," Park Ridge, Illinois, 1976.

lacking, or uninspired, on the subject of health and healing in and through the congregation.

An early paper, from 1967, on "The Congregation as a Healing Community" in *Lutheran Social Welfare*, presents a discussion of values clarification and hopes for the best. A 1979 survey book called *The Lutheran Church in North America*, published by the Lutheran Academy for Scholarships, covers Lutherans and Politics; Ethos, Style, and Polity; Religion and Science; Social Action; Economic Life; and Education. I found no mention of health issues. The closest I uncovered was a brief account of Henry E. Muhlenberg as a budding botanist.

On the up side, both the Department of Church and Society of the Lutheran Church in America and the Division of Theological Studies of the LCUSA are engaged in major studies of bio-medical ethics. *Human Medicine*, by James B. Nelson, published in 1973 by Augsburg Publishing House, still sounds a fresh note on current ethical dilemmas.

Lutherans, especially the clinically trained counselors, together with several health centers have taken up interest in the hospice movement. The study document of the LCA and its continuing Commission are providing solid guidance toward a more holistic approach to "Aging and the Older Person."

An issue of *Viewpoints: Christian Perspectives on Social Concerns* of the ALC, was devoted to "Health Care" in 1978. Its most helpful articles included an initial one by Lowell H. Mays, "Theological Perspectives on Health Care." In it he restores a unitary definition of mission this way: "The concern of God for people who are ill is to be exhibited also by his chosen people, the church. The church functions under a threefold understanding of mission: 1) diaconea, which may be understood as service, or more properly in this context as mercy; 2) kerygma, proclamation, or for this context a prophetic voice; and 3) koinonia, community, or as used here, human solidarity."[23]

SUMMARY

Still captive to its tradition that health and healing efforts are part of the society's responsibility, or, when under church auspices, the work of interested individuals or voluntary associations, the Lutheran churches, their congregations and agencies, are, in the main, largely unaffected by new concepts of healing and holistic health.

Major contributions which have mildly altered the tradition are the practice of a major force of clinically trained pastors and chaplains, the rise of the human ecology and holistic health movements, and the reverse impact of preventive and simplified medical and health services from the overseas experience of the churches to the U.S.A.

Lutheran theology, which has miraculously survived the temptation to join American Christian redemptorist triumphalism, may yet enable the Lu-

---

[23]Lowell H. Mays, "Theological Perspectives on Health Care," in *Viewpoints: Christian Perspectives on Social Concerns–Health Care*, Augsburg, Minneapolis, 1978, p. 4.

theran churches to harness some energy to make a modest contribution to a critical time—so long as it takes itself seriously, as Martin Marty is wont to say, but not *too* seriously.

Robert Schultz may have it wrapped up best when he says:

> Here again the church's ministry of redemption is not proportional to its ministry of helping or curing. It remains valid and meaningful even when the church is not able to make any significant contribution to the cure of the situation. Care of the incurably ill, companionship with the dying, and consolation of those who grieve the death of their loved ones or other sorrows and injustices in this life are important and significant—even though the church has no apparent capacity to help heal much that is wrong in the situation.
>
> The church's ministries of healing must continue to demonstrate not so much that the church can win the battle, which often it cannot, but that the fight and the struggle are still going on and that God himself is in the battle. The church does this best when it concentrates its healing ministry in areas other than those which happen to be popular at the time. What needs to be demonstrated is not that the church is willing to go out in the company of the whole society to fight aged dragons whose teeth are dull and whose days are numbered in any case but rather that the church is willing to focus on those tasks no one else in society is willing to undertake. This was once true with the church, giving leadership on the cutting edge of caring, but today it seems to seek safer battles and less demanding tasks.[24]

SELECTED BIBLIOGRAPHY

Academy of Religion and Mental Health—Proceedings, 5th Symposium. *Research in Religion and Health*. Fordham University Press, 1963.

Alexander, William Menzies. *Demonic Possession in the New Testament*. Edinburgh: T & T Clark, 1902.

Anointing and Healing. Statement Adopted by the Adjourned Meeting of the 1960 Convention of the United Lutheran Church in America, June 25-27, 1962, Detroit, Michigan. Board of Publication of the United Lutheran Church in America.

Archbiship's Commission. *The Church's Ministry of Healing*. London: Church of England Information Board, 1958.

Balint, Michael. *The Doctor, His Patient, and the Illness*. New York: International Press, 1957.

Belgam, David (ed.). *Religion and Medicine*. Ames, Iowa: Iowa State University Press, 1967.

Boe, Paul. "The Obligation of the Church in Social Welfare." *Lutheran Social Welfare Quarterly*, Vol. 3, September 1963, No. 3.

Boggs, Wade H., Jr. *Faith, Healing, and the Christian Faith*. Richmond, Va.: John Knox Press, 1956.

Bruder, Ernest. *Ministering to Deeply Troubled People*. Philadelphia: Fortress Press, 1964.

Buttrick, George A. *God, Pain and Evil*. New York: Abingdon Press, 1966.

Cabot, Richard C. and Dicks, Russel L. *The Art of Ministering to the Sick*. New York: The Macmillan Co., 1944.

Calder, Peter Ritchie. *Medicine and Man*. New York: New American Library, 1959. Mentor Book.

Carlson, Rick J. "Toward a New Understanding of Health Within Limitations of Medicine." Magazine article, magazine unknown.

Cassler, Henry H. "Lutheran Clinical Pastoral Education." *Lutheran Social Welfare Quarterly*, Vol. 3, September, 1963, No. 3.

---

[24]Robert C. Schultz, "Therapy and Absolution: Issues of Healing and Redemption," *SPC Journal*, *LCUSA*, New York, Vol. 2., 1979, pp. 7-8.

Christian Presence in Medical Work in Asia Today. Report of Second East Asia Christian Medical Workers Conference. Tokyo, Japan: Obun Printing Co., 1967.

Dawson, George C. *Healing: Pagan and Christian.* New York: The Macmillan Co., 1935.

Dodd, Edward M. *The Gift of the Healer.* New York: Friendship Press, 1964.

Doniger, Simon (ed.). *Healing: Human and Divine.* New York: Association Press, 1957.

Doniger, Simon (ed.). *The Nature of Man in Theological and Psychological Perspectives.* New York: Harper and Brothers, 1962.

_____. *Religion and Health.* New York: Association Press, 1958.

Droege, Thomas. "The Coonoor Conference." *Lutheran Social Welfare,* Vol. 8, Spring 1948, No. 1.

_____. *That Thy Saving Health May Be Known.* Concordia Theological Monthly Occasional Papers No. 2, May, 1968.

Dunbar, Flanders. *Mind and Body: Psychosomatic Medicine.* New York: Random House, 1947.

Evangelical Lutheran Church in Tanzania. *Health and Healing.* The Report of the 1967 Makumira Consultation on the Healing Ministry of the Church. Arusha, Tanzania: Medical Board of the Evangelical Lutheran Church in Tanzania, 1967.

Feifel, Herman. *The Meaning of Death.* New York: McGraw Hill, 1959.

Fletcher, Joseph. *Morals and Medicine.* Princeton: Princeton University Press, 1954.

Frost, Evelyn. *Christian Healing.* London: Mowbray, 1954.

Garlick, Phyllis L. *Man's Search for Health.* London: The Highway Press, 1952.

Goldbrunner, Josef. *Holiness is Wholeness.* New York: Pantheon Books, 1955.

Haas, Harold I. *The Church and Mental Health.* The Lutheran Church-Missouri Synod Board of Social Welfare, 1967.

The Healing Arts and the Church. Proceedings of medical-theological retreat at Peaceful Valley, Colorado. St. Louis: Lutheran Medical Missions Association.

Hempel, Johannes. *Heilung als Symbol und Wirklichkeit im Biblischen Schrifteum.* Göttingen: Vandenhoeck und Ruprecht, 1958.

Hiltner, Seward. *Religion and Health.* New York: The Macmillan Co., 1943.

Hoch, Dorothee. *Healing and Salvation: An Investigation of Healing Miracles.* London: SCM Press, 1958.

Holman, E. J. *The Cry of the Third World.* Report submitted to Joint Lutheran Medical Consultation, February, 1976.

Ikin, A. Graham. *New Concepts of Healing.* New York: Association Press, 1956.

Jahoda, Marie. *Current Concepts of Positive Mental Health.* New York: Basic Books, 1958.

Jayne, W. A. *The Healing Gods of Ancient Civilizations.* New Haven, Conn.: Yale University Press, 1925.

Jenkins, Daniel T. *The Doctor's Profession.* London: Student Christian Movement Press, 1949.

Kelsey, Morton T. "The Healing Ministry Within the Church." *Journal of Religion and Health,* Vol. 9, April 1970, No. 2.

Knight, James A. *A Psychiatrist Looks at Religion and Health.* New York: Abingdon Press, 1964.

Koppelmann, Herman H. *LC-MS Medical Missions, History to 1958.* Chicago: Wheat Ridge Foundation, 1976.

Lambourne, R. A. *Community, Church, and Healing.* London: Darton, Longman and Todd, 1963.

Large, John Ellis. *The Ministry of Healing.* New York: Morehouse-Gorham Co., 1959.

Letts, Harold C. (ed.). *The Lutheran Heritage,* Vol. 2. Philadelphia: Muhlenberg Press, 1957.

_____. *Health Care in America: A National Illness.* Philadelphia: Lutheran Church in America, 1974.

Lutheran Church in America. *The Church in Social Welfare.* New York: Board of Social Ministry, LCA, 1964.

_____. *Man, Medicine and Theology.* A Series of Studies in Christian Social Responsibility. Board of Social Ministry, LCA, 1967.

Lutheran Council in the U.S.A. *Health Care For All Americans!* Testimony before the U.S. House Ways and Means Committee, July 2, 1974.

_____. *The Healing Ministry of the Church.* Department of Medical Mission Service, May, 1970.

Martin, Bernard. *Healing For You.* Richmond, Va.: John Knox Press, 1965.

_____. *The Healing Ministry of the Church.* Richmond, Va.: John Knox Press, 1960.

Maves, Paul B. (ed.). *The Church and Mental Health.* New York: Charles Scribner's Sons, 1953.

May, Edward. *I Was Sick and You Visited Me*. Minneapolis: Augsburg Publishing Co., 1968.
_____. *That Thy Saving Health May Be Known Among All Nations*. A Book of Worship Resources for Occasions which Emphasize the Healing Ministry of the Church. Chicago: The Wheat Ridge Foundation, 1967.

May, Edward and Bulle, W. F. (ed.). "Selected Papers of Interest to Participants in Medical Mission Study Program." Chicago: Wheat Ridge Foundation (mimeographed).

McCasland, S. Vernon. *By the Finger of God: Demon Possession and Exorcism in the Light of Modern Views of Mental Illness*. New York: The Macmillan Co., 1951.

McNeill, John T. *A History of the Cure of Souls*. New York: Harper and Brothers, 1951.

Miller, Haskell M. *Compassion and Community*. New York: Association Press, 1961.

Muedeking, George. "Lutheran Theology and Social Welfare." *Lutheran Social Welfare Quarterly*, Vol. 2, December 1962, No. 4.

Norstad, Fredric M. "The Hospital as a Healing Community." *Lutheran Social Concern*, Vol. 13, Winter 1973, No. 4.

_____. *The Lutheran Institute of Human Ecology*. Lutheran Medical Mission Society, 1968.

Pelikan, Jaroslav. *The Shape of Death: Life, Death, and Immortality in the Early Fathers*. New York: Abingdon Press, 1961.

Sandstedt, Daniel H. "The Lutheran Church and Clinical Pastoral Education." *Lutheran Theological Seminary Bulletin* 50:4-17, 1970.

Sarano, Jacques. *The Meaning of the Body*. Philadelphia: Westminster Press, 1966.

Scharlemann, Martin. *Healing and Redemption*. St. Louis: Concordia Publishing House, 1965.
_____. *The Theological and Historical Basis for Lutheran Welfare*. Department of Social Welfare, Lutheran Church-Missouri Synod, 1958.

Scherzer, Carl J. *Ministering to the Physically Sick*. Philadelphia: Fortress Press.
_____. *Ministering to the Dying*. Englewood Cliffs, N.J.: Prentice-Hall, 1963.

Schmemann, Alexander. *For the Life of the World: Sacraments and Orthodoxy*. New York: National Student Christian Federation, 1973.

Sharpe, William. *Medicine and the Ministry*. New York: Brothers, 1966.

Siirala, Aarne. *The Voice of Illness*. Philadelphia: Fortress Press, 1964.

Southard, Samuel. *Religion and Nursing*. Nashville: Broadman Press, 1959.

Spannaus, Ruben E. "Lutheran Welfare in the American Scene." *Lutheran Social Welfare Quarterly*, Vol. 1, Summer 1967, No. 2.

The American Lutheran Church. *Christian Faith and the Ministry of Healing*. Adopted by the Church Council, 1965.
_____. *Criteria for Evaluating Proposals for a National Health Care Program*. Commission on Church and Society, December 1971.

Thompson, G. S. *The Role of Christianity in Church-Related Social Services*. Concordia Seminar, 1966.

Tournier, Paul. *A Doctor's Case Book in the Light of the Bible*. New York: Harper and Row.
_____. *The Healing of Persons*. New York: Harper and Brothers.
_____. *The Meaning of Persons*. New York: Harper and Brothers, 1957.
_____. *The Whole Person in a Broken World*. New York: Harper and Row, 1964.

The United Presbyterian Church. *The Relation of Christian Faith to Health*. Adopted by the 172nd General Assembly, May 1960. New York: Board of National Missions, 475 Riverside Drive.

Van Buskirk, James D. *Religion, Healing and Health*. New York: The Macmillan Co., 1952.

Viewpoints: Christian Perspectives on Social Concerns—Health Care. Minneapolis: Augsburg Publishing House, 1978.

Warren, Max A. C. *The Christian Imperative*. New York: Charles Scribner's Sons, 1955.
_____. *Interpreting the Cross*. London: SCM Press, 1966.

Weatherhead, Leslie D. *Psychology, Religion and Healing*. New York: Abingdon Press, 1951.

Westberg, Granger. *Minister and Doctor Meet*. New York: Harper and Brothers, 1961.
_____. *Nurse, Pastor and Patient*.
_____. (ed.). *Theological Roots of Wholistic Health Care*. Wholistic Health Centers, Inc., 1979.

White, Dale (ed.). *Dialogue in Medicine and Theology*. New York: Abingdon Press, 1967.

Wiehe, Vernon R. "The Congregation as a Healing Community." *Lutheran Social Welfare Quarterly*, Vol. 1, Summer 1967, No. 2.

Williams, Daniel Day. *The Minister and the Care of Souls*. New York: Harper and Brothers, 1961.

Wilson, Michael. *The Church Is Healing*. London: SCM Press, 1966.

Wise, Carroll. *Religion in Illness and Health*. New York: Harper and Brothers, 1942.

World Council of Churches. *The Healing Church*. World Council Studies No. 3. The Report of the Tuebingen Consultation, 1964. Geneva: World Council of Churches, 1964.

Dr. David Edwin Harrell, Jr.

CHAPTER IV

Healing in Protestant America

by David Edwin Harrell, Jr.

The interest of most American Protestant churches in health has been casual and sporadic. At the institutional level the work of Protestants in the health field has been overshadowed by the Catholic church. Of the 908 denominational hospitals in the country in 1940 only fifty-eight were operated by Protestant churches.[1] Of course most Protestant churches were relatively small and not well equipped to bear the large financial burdens of a modern medical center, but the lack of interest has other ideological roots. In comparison, for instance, Protestant Americans have been prolific builders of colleges. Education has been at the heart of the American Protestant mind, but healing, until recent years, became increasingly secular. In general, the changing views of American Protestants about health have been a part of the Christian accommodation of modern science.

American Protestants brought with them to the new world a unitary view of man (not neatly separating the physical and the spiritual) and a thoroughly supernatural view of health and sickness. Seventeenth-century Christians were not far removed from the faith of the Middle Ages. Catholic theologian Carlstadt rejected out of hand the early medical profession, advising "whoso falls sick shall use no physic, but commit his case to God, praying that His will be done."[2] The early English *Book of Common Prayer* urged ministers to exhort their flocks not "to kindle God's wrath," lest they "provoke him to plague us with divers diseases and sundry kinds of death."[3] Both Catholics and Protestants of the Reformation period believed that God healed supernaturally in a variety of ways. Particularly efficacious was the "royal touch" which was regarded as a source of thousands of miraculous cures in the early modern period, although William III of England was so skeptical of his own powers that he once told an anxious petitioner: "God give you better health and more sense."[4] More common were sacramental and liturgical healings which have

---

[1]E. H. L. Corwin, *The American Hospital* (New York: The Commonwealth Fund, 1946), pp. 45-46.

[2]Andrew W. White, *A History of the Warfare of Science with Theology* (New York: George Braziller, 1955), p. 46.

[3]*Ibid.*, p. 64.

[4]*Ibid.*, p. 48.

remained a minor part of the European Protestant tradition but were never very prominent in America.[5]

This supernaturalistic view of health and sickness flourished in Puritan New England. Specters, demons, witches, and other evil spirits were ever present in the world of the seventeenth century and were viewed as the cause of most of man's troubles. In 1693, Cotton Mather, the intellectual leader of seventeenth-century America, published *Wonders of the Invisible World* which included an explanation of the cause of epidemics:

> Plagues are some of those woes, with which the Devil troubles us. It is said of the Israelites, in 1 Cor. 10:10, *They were destroyed of the destroyer.* That is, they had the Plague among them. 'Tis the Destroyer, or the Devil, that scatters Plagues about the World: Pestilential and Contagious Diseases, 'tis the Devil, who do's oftentimes invades us with them. 'Tis no uneasy thing, for the Devil, to impregnate the Air about us, with such Malignant Salts, as meeting with the Salt of our Microcosm, shall immediately cast us into that Fermentation and Putrefaction, which will utterly dissolve All the Vital Types within us, Ev'n as an Aqua Fortis, made with a conjunction of Nitre and Vitriol, Corrodes what it Siezes upon. And when the Devil has raised those Arsenical Fumes, which become Venomous Quivers full of Terrible Arrows, how easily can he shoot the deleterious Miasms into those Juices or Bowels of Men's Bodies, which will soon Enflame them with a Mortal Fire! Hence come such Plagues, as that Beesome of Destruction which within our memory swept away such a throng of people from one English City in one Visitation: and hence those Infectious Feavers, which are but so many Disguised Plagues among us, Causing Epidemical Desolations.[6]

As late as the end of the eighteenth century John Wesley argued that "giving up witchcraft is giving up the Bible."[7]

Such religious leaders represented the most sophisticated tip of the American society. Beneath these intellectuals festered a society of rampant superstition and ignorance. In the seventeenth century many Americans still believed in and practiced forms of magic, spiritualism, herbalism, and astrology. A 1703 almanac reported:

For Country-men regard the Sign,
As though 'Twere Oracle Divine.[8]

And it is clear that some colonial Americans did practice witchcraft. In a sermon delivered in 1689 Cotton Mather acknowledged that New Englanders had many occult practices available to them, including witchcraft, enchantments, and charms. But he assured even weak Christians that they were not defenseless against occult practices and the temptation to use them: "There are three admirable *Amulets* that I can heartily recommend unto you all: *A fervent Prayer . . . A Lively Faith . . .* [and] *A Holy Life."* He continued:

---

[5]William A. Clebsch, "American Religion and the Cure of Souls," in William G. McLoughlin and Robert N. Bellah, eds., *Religion in America* (Boston: Houghton Mifflin Company, 1968), p. 253.

[6]White, *Warfare of Science,* p. 85.

[7]*Ibid.,* p. 167.

[8]Quoted in Jon Butler, "Magic, Astrology, and the Early American Religious Heritage, 1600-1760," *American Historical Review,* LXXXIV (April, 1979), p. 330.

Use these things as the Shields of the Lord. . . . Suppose now that any *Witches* may let fly their Curses at you, you are now, like a *Bird* on the *Wing,* in such Heavenward Motions that they cannot hit you. Now the *Devils* and their Creatures cannot say of you, as the *Demon* said of the Christian Woman whom, at a *Stageplay* he took Possession of, and being asked, gave this reason of his taking her, *I found her on my own ground.*[9]

Occult practices declined in the course of the eighteenth century, partly as a result of coercion by the state, but, as a modern student of the phenomenon says, "The emphasis on healing that Cotton Mather believed accounted for the colonial wise man's success remained strong as America entered the industrial age."[10] Patent medicine, pseudo-sciences like phrenology, and a number of other healing fads combined with new Christian forms of healing to offer supernaturalistic hope for the common people of the nineteenth century.

Considering the superstition and ignorance of the time, seventeenth-century Protestant reactions to medical science were fairly enlightened. Martin Luther defended the use of medicine: "Do you eat when you are hungry: Even so you may use physic, which is God's gift just as meat and drink is, or whatever else we use for the preservation of life."[11] In the judgement of one historian, Luther's stand was responsible for the early advancement of anatomical studies in the German cities.[12] In spite of his persistent belief in witches, Cotton Mather was a staunch supporter of medical science. He early accepted Newtonian physics and his defense of smallpox inoculation was a crucial milestone in early American medical history. The Puritan accommodation of scientific thought was so thorough and complete, according to James Ward Smith, that "by 1700 Puritan Harvard was teaching the new science and on the whole teaching it well."[13]

In general, American Protestants established a friendly relationship with the scientific revolution from 1600 to 1850. Although the partnership was always slightly uneasy, Protestant ministers accepted scientists as helpful junior partners. Religious leaders tolerated, even marveled at, new discoveries of useful knowledge, but science remained a sideshow and religion remained center stage. Perry Miller described the seventeenth-century Puritan attitude toward science: "In short, they took little part either in advancing new theories or in retarding their development. . . . The whole matter was regarded as indifferent or secondary."[14] The specialization of knowledge in the modern world, the "chopping up" so characteristic of modernity, increasingly separated healing from religion, as it did other areas of scientific expertise, but

---

[9]*Ibid.*, p. 332.

[10]*Ibid.*, p. 346.

[11]White, *Warfare of Science*, p. 46.

[12]*Ibid.*

[13]"Religion and Science in American Philosophy," in James Ward Smith and A. Leland Jamison, eds., *The Shaping of American Religion* (Princeton: Princeton University Press, 1961), p. 413.

[14]*Ibid.*, p. 414.

most Protestant leaders did not feel threatened by these intrusions. Theology still reigned supreme at mid-nineteenth century.

As the corpus and influence of modern science grew, American Protestant theologians embraced and used it. The study of natural theology blossomed and theologians pointed out how each new scientific discovery reinforced traditional Christian dogma. God's revelation of Himself in nature paralleled His revelation of Himself in the Bible. Since the two could not be contradictory, for two hundred and fifty years Protestant theologians worked diligently at the increasingly difficult task of reconciling science and religion. Herbert Hovenkamp, in his study of science and religion in the early nineteenth-century, described this preoccupation: "In this way nineteenth-century American Protestantism conducted a broad experiment in the unification of knowledge and belief. Above all, Protestants tried to create a religion free from all doubt. The orthodox Protestant did not want to confess anything he could not prove, so he devised a 'scientific theology' that could prove everything."[15]

This unification of science and theology was increasingly done at the expense of theology. While scientific discoveries might reinforce revelation, and while theology might be scientifically respectable, science increasingly whittled away at the domain of the supernaturalism and increasingly confined religion to questions of morality and metaphysics. Nowhere was the advance of science more apparent by the end of the nineteenth-century than in medicine. While most mainstream Protestants continued to offer lip service to the supernatural healing available to Christians, and all marveled at the ways in which medical science demonstrated the power of God, American Protestants generally conceded that health was the concern of God's servants, the physicians. It is significant that of the 178 hospitals in the nation in 1873 only seven were operated by churches.[16]

This accommodation of science and religion, one which increasingly stripped religion of its authority, was a fragile and superficial one. Up until the end of the nineteenth century American scientists worked primarily in the applied sciences and offered little theoretical challenge to Christian thought. But as the facts accumulated, they became harder and harder to digest within the old religious system. By 1860, writes Hovenkamp, "the experiment had clearly failed. The facts that looked like the great hope of Christianity in 1800 proved to be its nemesis a half century later. American Protestants had attempted to make religion into a science. It became, however, a pseudoscience, whose 'facts' would not hold up in the face of the more convincing facts of geology or biology."[17]

Even more important, in the last half of the nineteenth century the American mind was powerfully influenced by a series of revolutionary new theories and American Protestantism for the first time took "science seriously," ap-

[15]Herbert Hovenkamp, *Science and Religion in America, 1800-1860* ([Philadelphia]: University of Pennsylvania Press, 1978), p. x.

[16]Corwin, *American Hospital,* p. 7.

[17]*Science and Religion,* p. x.

plying the scientific method to theology and metaphysics.[18] The method behind Charles Lyell's work in geology and Charles Darwin's in biology undermined the whole concept of natural theology in the late nineteenth century. Hovenkamp writes: "As positivism and uniformitarianism began to demand that every observable effect be explained by a natural cause, . . . illustrations of God's government and watchfulness became much more difficult to maintain. In a world where natural causes prevailed and differential equations could be used to describe processes that had gone on for endless ages without being affected by any transcendental agent, the whole idea of a God watching over his creatures started to lose any referential meaning."[19]

Placed in particular jeopardy by the new wide-ranging application of the scientific method was the miracle. Many nineteenth century intellectuals came to wonder "how scientific explanation could be possible for one who allowed miracles into his system."[20] Advances in medical science contributed greatly to the demise of the miracle. Andrew D. White, writing in 1895 and himself a product of the new era of scientific confidence, illustrated this scientific optimism: "The world is hardly beyond the beginning of medical discoveries, yet they have already taken from theology what was formerly its strongest province—sweeping away from this vast field of human effort that belief in miracles which for more than twenty centuries has been the main stumblingblock in the path of medicine; and in doing this they have cleared higher paths not only for science, but for religion."[21]

Impressed and intimidated by the accomplishments of science and the new scientific philosophies—pragmatism, instrumentalism, and positivism—sophisticated American Protestants abandoned much that had long been central to theology. "Protestantism disowned metaphysics," wrote James Ward Smith, "and proclaimed a 'Religion of Humanity' and a 'Social Gospel.' "[22] In a sense, late nineteenth-century liberal religion was a final capitulation to science.

The development of liberal theology and the social gospel provided a new foundation for understanding the role of Christianity in healing. But influential as the social gospel was on mainstream American Protestantism in the twentieth century, it was only the latest of three distinctive theological patterns which survived into the twentieth century. Each represented a different degree of accommodation of science; each had its own understanding of the role of religion in health; each survives in American Protestantism today.

Some American Protestants have remained isolated from the centuries of scientific thought, knowing only that scientific theories are gibberish to them and that they have little access to its millennialistic promises. Isolated from the mainstream of American life by poverty and a lack of education, many twen-

[18]Smith, "Religion and Science," p. 404.
[19]*Science and Religion*, p. 95.
[20]*Ibid.*, p. 91.
[21]*Warfare of Science*, p. 66.
[22]"Religion and Science," p. 424.

tieth-century Americans live in the same anti-scientific, supernatural world of the seventeenth century poor. Nowhere was the continuing potence of supernaturalism more apparent than in the explosion of pentecostal sects in the early twentieth century among American poor whites and blacks. Highly millennialistic and other-worldly, pentecostals believed that the mainstream churches had compromised with "the world" and lost their faith in God. While few Pentecostals were sophisticated enough to recognize their enemy, it was scientific rationalism. A recent pentecostal historian writes: "When they protested against Higher Criticism, Darwinism, and the Social Gospel, against ecumenicalism and declining morality in the Church," they were in fact protesting scientific rationalism, bureaucracy, and secularism. In short, what they deplored in the Church were those very "characteristics that typify modern urban culture."[23]

Thoroughly suspicious of modern thought, alienated from society by poverty, and denied the services of medical science, it is understandable that pentecostals introduced as a major theme in their teaching the concept of miraculous healing. Pentecostals believed that healing was secured by the scourging of Christ, the prooftext being 1 Peter 2:24: "Who his own self bare our sins in his own body on the tree . . . by whose stripes we were healed." Healing might come through laying on of hands by one having the "gift of healing," anointing with oil by elders, application of "prayer handkerchiefs," "aprons," or other articles deemed to have special significance, or simply by the "prayer of faith" of the individual believer.[24] During their early years, pentecostals generally rejected the use of doctors as a sign of weakness in faith.

The fervor of the pentecostal revival of the early twentieth century waned in the 1930's and 1940's as did the confidence in divine healing, although sensational healing testimonies continued to be published. But after World War II a tremendous new healing revival broke out among American pentecostals—a revival that ultimately had a world-wide impact. The revival was led by a coterie of pentecostal evangelists who established huge independent ministries based on their prowess as healers. Scores of talented ministers, the most successful of whom was Oral Roberts, crisscrossed the country in the 1950's and 1960's holding tent revivals and laying hands on hundreds of thousands of believers to "deliver them from sickness." In his early years Roberts specialized in casting out demons; he claimed a sensitivity in his right hand which gave him the "power to detect the presence, names and numbers of demons" in sick people.[25] In the mid-1960's the more sophisticated independent healing ministers began to moderate their claims and they played a major role in the emergence of the charismatic movement which shall be discussed later, but

---

[23]Robert Mapes Anderson, *Vision of the Disinherited* (New York and Oxford: Oxford University Press, 1979), p. 224.

[24]*Ibid.*, p. 93.

[25]See Reg G. Hanson, "Wm. Branham Attends Roberts Campaign in Tampa, Florida," *Healing Waters*, III (March, 1949), 6 and "Demons," *America's Healing Magazine*, VIII (September, 1954), 2.

scores of healing revivalists still minister to the most deprived segments of American Protestantism, offering them salvation from sin, healing, health, and financial blessings. While many of the evangelists of the post-war period, most notably Roberts, tried to combine religious healing with an approval of medical science, many did not.[26] In December, 1979, in Birmingham, Alabama, evangelist Robert Schamback told a revival audience that they should not spend "a penny on medicine before the Lord comes."[27]

The range of healing testimonials offered by pentecostals was as broad as medical science, although the evangelists had their homespun medical jargon which combined many illnesses under such terms as "a heart condition," "nervous disorders," and "cancerous tumors." Frequently sufferers supported multiple healings. In a somewhat exaggerated example, one grateful believer wrote:

> I shall try to enumerate some of the things the Spirit revealed and the healing power of Jesus delivered me from them. Blood clot, mastoid trouble, sciatic nerve trouble, many pains in the body because of the injury thirteen years before, chronic throat trouble, chronic sores that bled inside my nose, stigmatism in my eyes and nervous jerking in right eyelid due to strain. I also was healed of kidney trouble, sinus, gastric condition in the bowels, athlete's foot, and a bad rectal trouble. I also suffered an injury to my ankle during the revival and the Lord healed that, also a very tired feeling in my shoulders. Many are telling me how much better I look, and I thank God I can tell them how much better I feel. Surely the Lord has given me a general overhauling.[28]

Testimonies of resurrections from the dead were numerous in the movement.

While few would question the impact such religious beliefs might have on those suffering psychic or nervous disturbances, serious doubts have been cast on the efficacy of pentecostal healings. The movement has been extremely introspective in recent years and many insiders have raised serious questions about the thousands of healing testimonials. In the 1960's charge after charge of fraudulent claims and exploitation were published in pentecostal magazines. Donald Gee, respected international pentecostal leader, wrote: "The popular healing campaigns have produced over the years such grave scandals that it will need all the courage, and wisdom, and humility that God can give Pentecostal leadership to cleanse them away. What ought to have been our glory has become our shame."[29] External investigators have been even more skeptical. In 1925, a panel of twenty-three ministers, doctors, and professors investigated 350 alleged healings claimed during a revival by healer-evangelist Charles S. Price. "Of that number," reported historian Robert M. Anderson, "the committee found that 5 had become insane, 39 had died, 17 were worse, 212 showed 'no change,' 38 showed some improvement, and 5 were consid-

---

[26]See David Edwin Harrell, Jr., *All Things Are Possible: The Healing and Charismatic Revivals in Modern America* (Bloomington and London: Indiana University Press [1975]).

[27]Sermon, December 1, 1979, Boutwell Auditorium, Birmingham, Alabama.

[28]Thelma Chaney, *The Power of God on Exhibition* (Tulsa: TOP Service, 1954).

[29]"The Value of the Supernatural," *Pentecost*, No. 62 (December, 1962-February, 1963), 17.

ered cured." The committee concluded that "no case had benefitted that could not have received the same benefit by methods known to medical science."[30] In more recent years physician William Nolen reached similar conclusions after investigating reported healings in a Kathryn Kuhlman campaign.[31]

Whatever the efficacy of faith healing, it obviously remains a major American Protestant approach to healing, sometimes combined with medical care, but in the case of several million poor Americans, it is the only readily available source of healing and health. In many underdeveloped nations faith in supernatural Christian healing combines easily with forms of native healing. In short, some American Christians and many people living in the underdeveloped areas of the world still hold essentially prescientific views of healing, either regarding medical science as outright heresy or a secondary and limited source of good health.

The second mode of Protestant adaptation to medical science in the twentieth century, perhaps best typified by evangelicals, is a continuation of the nineteenth century quest for the unification of religion and science. By no means all Protestants capitulated to science at the end of the nineteenth century; the struggle for a reasonable natural theology has continued with a great vigor in the twentieth century. Embarrassed by the most rabid fundamentalists, stereotyped as ignoramuses, American evangelicals have struggled desperately (if not altogether successfully in the eyes of intellectuals) to defend the reasonableness of traditional Christianity against the onslaught of "science, falsely so called." The post-World War II neo-evangelical boom; the emergence of Billy Graham, superstar; and the construction of a gigantic evangelical parochial school system in the 1970's all testify, in different ways, to the persistence of this nineteenth century form of thought.

Anachronistic as it seems in the twentieth century, and certainly not typical of mainline evangelicals, Christian Science was a logical outgrowth of such thinking. Deeply indebted to the nineteenth-century pseudosciences, Christian Science appealed to the basic assumptions of many nineteenth-century Americans. It called for a return both to "true Christianity" and a revelation of "true science." What set Christian Science apart from the mainstream denominations of America in the late nineteenth century was its concentration on the problem of health. Christian Science called into question medical science while most American Christians saw other issues as more threatening. But in the "wealthier, citified denominations" its unification of religion and science, and its promise of health, found a ready audience.[32]

Most American evangelicals thought Christian Science was absurd. The life or death struggle was with biologists, archaeologists, geologists, and Biblical critics. That remains the battleground today. In a sense, medical science

---

[30]*Vision*, p. 94.
[31]William A. Nolen, *A Doctor in Search of a Miracle* (New York: Random House, 1975).
[32]Clebsch, "American Religion," p. 254.

has always been the least threatening of all scientific thought. The applied nature of medicine caused little difficulty for most evangelicals, revealing, they believed, the marvelous working of God in nature and threatening none of their basic assumptions.

In short, evangelical Christians still have little difficulty believing that medicine is God's way of relieving man's physical problems and that the church's business of saving souls is infinitely more important. Evangelicalism is the best example of the religious compartmentalization of modern life. Evangelical churches have been tremendously influential in the development of educational and missionary institutions in the United States but have made little contribution to the development of health care. According to the *Yearbook of American Churches,* in 1972 American Protestant churches budgeted nearly three times as much money for education as they did for "health."[33] At most, medical care has been used as a tool to aid missions. The care of the body was properly in the hands of the physician, though not out of God's control, and doctors, like other Christians, served best when they led men to God.

The growth of theological liberalism in America in the late nineteenth century opened the way for a third accommodation with medical science. Almost completely discarding the supernaturalism of traditional Christianity, and feeling no antagonism toward science, liberal Protestants turned their attention to a search for the good life. James Ward Smith recalled: "The present writer, reared in devout Protestant surroundings, well remembers the most frequent precept of his early religious training in the 1920's and 1930's: 'Religion consists in a life well led.' "[34]

In its most highly developed forms, the social gospel completely humanized the Christian message. And yet, to a remarkable degree, the social gospel disregarded the issue of health. Amid the vast literature of the movement and the myriads of committees and organizations formed to reform society, one is at a loss to find much said about basic health issues.[35] In fact, the social gospelers were obsessed with economic and social injustice. Economic deprivation made people unhealthy and might momentarily raise health issues, but most of the reforms of the early twentieth century concentrated on the larger social problems.

The social gospelers' interest in broad sociological questions was partly related to the development of that discipline in the universities of the late nineteenth century. Equipped with new ideas and vocabularies in their search for social justice, the liberal Protestants of the early twentieth century were prepared only for that particular kind of battle. Furthermore, liberal Protestants more or less capitulated to science and had little inclination to invade the realm

---

[33]Constant H. Jacquet, Jr., ed., *Yearbook of American Churches 1976* (Nashville: Abingdon [1976]), p. 260.
[34]"Religion and Science," p. 430.
[35]All of the major studies of the social gospel movement are silent on the question of health. See, for instance, Aaron Ignatius Abell, *The Urban Impact of American Protestantism 1865-1900* (Hamden and London: Archon, 1962).

of the physician. The chief health message of the social gospel was that the benefits of medical science, along with other modern advances, ought to be made available to all people as a matter of social justice.

Probably the most important practical outgrowth of the social gospel was the institutional church. Institutional churches emerged in most major American cities in the late nineteenth century, providing general educational and cultural services. Although the most typical new ministries of institutional churches were kindergartens, day care centers, cultural lectures on sociology and economics, and aid to labor organizations, they also sometimes offered health services, generally a clinic in which charity medical services were offered at the church building. No one has yet studied the impact or evolution of these churches. Neither is it possible to establish any relationship between the social gospel and the building of denominational hospitals. It is clear that the Roman Catholic church maintained its overwhelming predominance in that area.[36]

What did emerge within liberal Protestantism in the early twentieth century was a clearer role for the minister as a pastoral counselor. Historian William A. Clebsch believes that the development of the pastoral role has taken a peculiar turn in America and that liberal religion has had a far greater impact by the development of counseling than through its more publicized political activities. Clergymen are important members of the "helping professions" and have carved out a niche in American life which is important in the "cure of souls" and holds great promise, believes Clebsch, for the future.[37]

"Modern religion," writes Clebsch, "inherits four types of the cure of souls from the entire range of Western religion: healing, guiding, sustaining, and reconciling."[38] Healing in a sacramental sense has never been a strong part of American religion, and faith healing, for all of its appeal to the disinherited, has never gained respectability. Liberal religion in America, then, essentially abandoned the healing function: "Rene Descartes' sharp dichotomy between matter and spirit split physical medicine from religion, and after Louis Pasteur medical efficacy became so demonstratable that many moderns have thought religious healing to be occult or even deluded."[39]

Clebsch also believes that the "helping professions with psychotherapeutic orientations are similarly invading the arena of pastoral guidance."[40] The absence of rigid religious ethical standards in an increasingly secular society means that psychotherapists or pastoral counselors trained in psychotherapy are often more successful than traditional religious counselors: "Pastoral guiding in contemporary America is faltering not from unwillingness to be helpful, but from having found no way of relating the will of God to the welfare of man

---

[36]See Jacquet, ed., *Yearbook of American Churches*, p. 253. It seems significant that the *Yearbook* says nothing about the health activities of Protestant churches in America.
[37]"American Religion," pp. 250-252.
[38]*Ibid.*, p. 252.
[39]*Ibid.*
[40]*Ibid.*, p. 254.

in a swiftly changing, bafflingly complex, and eudemonistic (perhaps even hedonistic) society. The psychotherapists' advantage lies finally in their being professionally and ideologically unconcerned about the will of God, and thus single-mindedly given to the welfare of their clients."[41]

On the other hand, Clebsch believes that the pastoral role is more important than ever in modern society in "sustaining" those "whose lives seem to be falling apart because of some ominous disruption" and in "reconciling" people with deep interpersonal problems. American congregationalism is particularly fitted for the role of sustaining because it provides a homogenous community for support. The key social role of the minister in American society (in marriage and death) makes him an essential helper in reconciliation. "Proficiency . . ." writes Clebsch, "in the cure of souls is the goal to be sought by shifting the conceptual emphasis from remedying debilities to that of developing spiritual strengths."[42]

The development of wholistic health, it seems to me, is a natural culmination of this liberal Christian emphasis. While wholistic health advocates have no reservations about the validity of medical science, they argue that religion plays a part in healing, or, more importantly, in health. The wholistic health approach assigns specialized roles to physicians, psychotherapists, and ministers, insisting that "God is a partner in the healing process."[43] The pastoral counselor is "an equal member of the healing team" who makes sure that "the spiritual dimensions are given equal attention." The key to the wholistic concept is a proper cooperation between medicine and pastoral counseling. In the words of Granger Westberg: "The strength of this particular model is that the unique gift of healing which belongs to the church is exercised in the closest kind of relationship to competent medical care. The pastoral counselor can legitimately focus on value questions that relate to the meaning of life, helping people see how the stress in their lives is related to matters of value and meaning. At the same time the best of medical care is provided the patient at a Wholistic Health Care Center."[44]

Finally, the post-World War II period has produced a new intellectual crisis, causing what sociologists have called a serious "dislocation" among western intellectuals. For a variety of reasons, the euphoric optimism of the nineteenth century, which was strongly related to the seemingly boundless accomplishments of science, died in the mid-twentieth century. Partly, the modern malaise was caused by the monstrous social, economic, and military tragedies of the twentieth century. "The real source of the revival of art and religion after World War II," writes James Ward Smith, "has been a disillusionment with science which began with the depression and culminated at Hiroshima."[45] For all of its promises, science had not solved the problems of

[41]*Ibid.*, p. 256.

[42]*Ibid.*, p. 264.

[43]Granger E. Westberg, ed., *Theological Roots of Wholistic Health Care* (Hinsdale, Ill.: Wholistic Health Centers, Inc., [1979]), p. 3.

[44]*Ibid.*, p. 31.

[45]"Religion and Science," p. 438.

starvation, war, human greed, and death. Of course, science never promised so much, but men who had welcomed it as the messiah became increasingly angry because it gave less than they had expected.

Perhaps more serious were new intellectual challenges to the basic assumptions of western thought. By the middle of the twentieth century scientists had riddled the orderly world of Newtonian physics and by the 1960's a "new physics" had emerged which clearly questioned the scientific method. The new science seemed to doubt the validity of all external observation. But the assault on the basic assumptions of western thought was broad as well as deep. Sociologist Allan W. Eister writes: "Not just religious assertions or dogmas (or even quite different kinds of statements, such as scientific propositions) have been challenged. In philosophy—in logical positivism, for example—the fundamental processes involved in conceptualizing experience are now seen to be a matter of social invention, complicated by the presence of non-rational, irrational, and even anti-rational preferences and responses among humans."[46]

The disenchantment of American intellectuals with traditional forms of thought was pervasive—for instance, in the development of modern art and the use of new literary forms. In the minds of many American intellectuals in the late twentieth century the premier question was whether or not there could be such a thing as rational communication, and their most persistent search was for other, non-rational, forms of knowledge. Intellectuals tolerate such serious dislocations better than others, and while most people might not discard so easily the basic beliefs of their society, they nonetheless feel disoriented when their leaders lose confidence in the basic intellectual assumptions of their day. In a sense, argues Eister, the intellectuals of a society are the keepers of the gate, who suppress heretical new ideas by proving them to be at odds with the known truths of the day. When the intellectuals lose their confidence in their own set of truths, they communicate their lack of confidence in peripheral ways, but, more important, they no longer stand in the gap to protect the society against the non-rational thought that bubbles up from beneath. In a very real sense science has lost its role as the infallible arbiter in modern thought.[47]

Nowhere is the new intellectual uncertainty more obvious than in the area of medicine. Physicians have shown an increased interest in non-scientific health care, particularly in systems which either predate modern medicine or exist in societies which have never accepted science as authoritarian. The recent announcement by the *New England Journal of Medicine* that Harvard cardiologist Herbert Benson was about to begin a three year study of the "health practices and beliefs of other eras and cultures" highlighted modern medical flexibility. According to news reports, Benson "believes that ancient

---

[46]"Culture Crises and New Religious Movements: A Paradigmatic Statement of a Theory of Cults," in Irving I. Zaretsky and Mark P. Leone, eds., *Religious Movements in Contemporary America* (Princeton: Princeton University Press [1974],) p. 620.
[47]*Ibid.*, pp. 612-627.

72

healing methods and even witchcraft-like techniques could produce safe and inexpensive alternatives to modern medicine."[48]

It is in this context that the holistic health movement is best understood. Essentially committed to the belief that "all modalities of healing, ancient as well as modern, deserve scientific exploration and should be used where appropriate,"[49] holistic health typifies the syncretic capacity of the modern mind. The movement includes combinations unthinkable a generation earlier. Dr. Milton Fried of Atlanta, who is both a doctor and a chiropractor, told a local reporter: "It's like being a Protestant and a Catholic at the same time in Northern Ireland."[50] Although holistic health easily encompasses "faith healing" and other religious forms, its unifying theme is healing lore and its interest in religion is casual. The clientele of the holistic movement is remarkedly like that of Christian Science in the nineteenth century. An official at the Atlanta Federal Health Center characterized the movement in terms that would have easily fit early Christian Science: "The holistic people reach this small group in the middle class who are very concerned about their health. These people stopped smoking, they are into running and into the environment, they drive with their seat belts on. They may be weller than they were when they started (holistic services), but they were pretty well to start with."[51]

More central to the religious experience of modern America has been the emergence of a wide variety of new sects and cults. Combined they form a movement so formidable it has been labelled "the current American Metaphysical Movement."[52] The range of popular religious groups which have flourished in the twentieth century includes: "(1) the churches founded on the margins of nineteenth-century American Protestantism which maintain active memberships today, such as Christian Science, Spiritualism, Mormonism, some genres of Pentecostalism, New Thought Movements; (2) recently founded religious groups such as Scientology, sidewalk churches, Youth for Jesus movements; (3) syncretistic groups based on imported cults such as Santeria, Meher Baba, Hare Krishna which are active in many American urban centers."[53] While there are considerable differences among these groups, most of them display a non-rational base in which "altered states of consciousness are . . . highly prized and cultivated" and most of them emphasize spiritual healing.[54]

The astonishing growth of the charismatic movement in modern America is a part of the same craving for supernatural religious experience. Born in the

[48]"Witchcraft on the Rise in Africa; Modern Medicine Men Find Out Why," *Chronicle of Higher Ecucation*, XIX (November 5, 1979), 14.

[49]Harold H. Bloomfield and Robert B. Kory, *The Holistic Way to Health & Happiness* (New York: Simon and Schuster [1978]), p. 55.

[50] Suzanne Dolezal, "Holistic Healing Means Fine-Tuning Your Body," *Atlanta Journal*, June 19, 1979, p. 2-B.

[51]*Ibid.*, p. 1-B.

[52]Zaretsky and Leone, eds., *Religious Movement*, p. xii.

[53]*Ibid.*

[54]*Ibid.*, p. xiv. For a discussion of the healing emphasis in the cults, see pp. 275-458.

womb of the small Pentecostal churches in the post-World War II period, the Pentecostal experience which features non-rational states of ecstasy and miraculous healing found a ready reception among middle-class Americans in the post-war years. Oral Roberts' immense financial empire, capped by the construction of the $125 million "City of Faith" health complex and medical school, is supported by over 3,000,000 regular contributing "partners." The Roberts clientele is larger than most American churches. His empire was built on the challenge to "expect a miracle." And Roberts was only the tip of the huge charismatic surge in the America and the world in the 1960's and 1970's that was built on a growing search for a supernatural key to health which would supplement, if not replace, scientific medicine.[55]

In summary, American Protestantism has reacted to the advances of medical science in modern history in a variety of ways. Many poor Americans, essentially alienated both from modern thought and the health services available to the affluent, have continued to live in a supernaturalistic, frequently anti-rational, world. God is their hope and Christ is their healer. Second, many American Protestants still live in a nineteenth-century world in which science and religion are separated; the one treating the physical side of man and discovering the natural laws which God has established; the other dealing with the infinitely more important business of saving souls. Typified by the evangelical churches, this wing of American Protestantism has never been more than superficially interested in health. Third, liberal Protestantism persistently has sought ways in which religion can serve man. Often preoccupied with economic and political questions, in recent years liberal Protestantism has taken new interest in religion's role in the cure of souls. Finally, the intellectual malaise of the twentieth century, its uncertainty and self-doubt, has opened a door for medical and religious experimentation which, in the words of one of the supporters of holistic health, "is one of the most exciting yet most potentially dangerous" facets of modern thought.[56] The ultimate expression of the modern religious spirit of individualism and voluntaryism, American Protestantism still offers a wide range of options to those who would entreat God's blessing to heal and preserve.

[55]See Harrell, *All Things Are Possible*.
[56]Bloomfield and Cory, *The Holistic Way*, p. 55.

Rev. Paul F. Goetting

CHAPTER V

The Christian Congregation as a Healing Community

by Paul F. Goetting

The Christian congregation is and has always been a healing community. And, it will always be. For where the Word is preached and believed, Christ is present. Where two or three are gathered in faith, Christ joins Himself to them and to each other in a unique relationship. That bond of love and community is both presently healing and certain of ultimate health. TO REALIZE MORE FULLY THIS HEALING PROCESS, AND TO INCREASE THE CERTAINTY OF ULTIMATE HEALTH is the purpose and focus of this presentation.

The treasure which the local congregation has from God is very simply the forgiveness of sins and the hope of the resurrection. It is Christ's forgiveness that makes the unity and creates the faith-fellowship. His forgiveness through the cross makes me acceptable and whole with God. And, it is in my being forgiven by others and my forgiving that enables me to be accepted and accepting of others. In this manner, God created the unusual community, the Holy Christian Church, the communion of Saints.

However,, the healing process of bandaging the mortal and spiritual wounds, the mending of broken bones and human relations, encounters the ultimate enemy, Death, as Christ Himself did. What would appear to be failure in the healing process becomes the ultimate cure: God makes life whole even in death! And, this is *the* mystery of faith, beyond imagination: The Christian community celebrating in life and in death the hope, the promise of absolute health and wholeness, the resurrection of the body.

A Christian Community, begun and continuing through the forgiveness of sins, functions in a multi-directional communication process. While originating from the cross, the message and action of forgiveness is a continuous interactive process, publicly spoken by the pastor before the congregation at every Sunday's Holy Communion, but also reverberating through the words and life-style of the faithful through the week, as Christians forgive and are forgiven.

The historical message of the Risen Christ is the basis of both our respective and collective ministries. As the apostles' ministry rested on their being witnesses to the resurrection, so this ministry continues through both clergy and lay. Baptized and alive in Him through faith, we celebrate His presence,

77

and know and share the promises He gives. Thus, whether clergy or medical doctor, social worker or construction worker, church secretary or corporate president, through each vocation we perform our ministries in the apostolic tradition as witnesses to His resurrection and to His promise of the resurrection of the body. In the family, in the neighborhood, and in our varied vocations, we are witnesses to the resurrection, in what we say and what we do, and the way we do what we say.

From the days of Jesus' ministry in Palestine till now, a community of humankind has shared the experience, each in many and different ways, yet all very similar to the Diseased Woman in Mark 5, the knowledge and experience that faith has made us whole! Whole in every sense. Even as we become sick, are depressed, and suffer pain, the wholeness goes on. The People of God trusting God, supporting each other, ministering to each other through Word and Sacraments and caring for one another with all the "goods" God gives, sustained by individual and common ministries, in the process of healing toward ultimate health.[1]

This is not mere doctrine or theological rhetoric. This is the experience of the Christian Church. I know it, and I am confident that you too know the healing of life and the renewal of the world through the forgiveness of sins and the hope of the resurrection shared in the local congregation.

However, perhaps at no other time in history have so many felt a need for community, and so few seem to find it. While all of us can, I am sure, point to those experiences of genuine healing in the fellowship of the local congregation, I suspect many of us can point to more times when we needed a spiritual accepting support group and did not find such. While in each congregation there is an element that feels good about the fellowship, there is evidence of a significant number of people in each parish who feel on the edge, distant and in many cases even alienated, if not hostile. Many of the latter are church shopping. There is the hearing of what the Gospel and the Church offer, but too few genuine experiences that lead one to believe and experience the great claims made. If I do not experience love, I cannot be very loving. If I am lonely, isolated, frightened, and need someone to touch me, and I enter a local church, and no one speaks to me, no one acknowledges my presence, no one accepts me, I could, and many do, conclude that the church is deceitful and a sham!

If you want to know what ought to be the church's priorities in mission, ask what is "falling through the cracks"—what basic human needs are not being met by anyone else at this time. Where I grew up in South St. Louis, Lutherans discovered during the Civil War that the sick and the orphaned were not being cared for. So they began a hospital and an orphanage. While orphanage support and the maintaining of hospitals may not now be a "fall-through-the-crack" need, there are many other clearly identifiable needs, not least is

---

[1] I do not want to imply that the fullest realization of community in a local parish is a cure-all for any disease, nor dare I speak as if the scientific role of medicine needs to give way to support groups as the new treatment for whatever ails an individual.

78

the cry for food and the inequitable distribution of medical care for the poor. While encouraging these, and the continued process of searching for new needs not being met, I want to argue that nothing is falling through the cracks more than the cry of people for community, for a sense of being accepted, supported by a caring spiritual fellowship.

Achieving programs of social service and social action are more likely if we can raise to a higher level a greater number of the membership who feel a sense of belonging, and are personally participating in the design and development of the parish's purpose and program. An authoritarian, dominant leadership may speak boldly and prophetically, only to have a sizable portion of the membership shrug their shoulders with apathy, or vote against the pronouncements by staying away and finding religion in other places.

While the local Christian congregation is indeed a healing community, we need to realize the full potential of the parish as an authentic community. We need to identify the blockages, those forces, traditions and behavioral patterns that inhibit larger numbers of people from having a more profound experience of community in the fellowship of the faith. A plaque in a pastor's study said it this way, "He who hopes for a good harvest, prays with hoe in hand." Our conviction that the local parish is a community and functions as such dare not inhibit a vigorous effort to realize community in our parishes. You do not have community because the preacher or the sign announces your church has it.

The Church is God's Holy People, and at one and the same time, a very human institution. We must wrestle Christian theology *and* at the same time the growing insights of those who study institutions, especially the church. We must keep a critical creative tension between the two.

The insights available from the discipline of organizational development and the general behavioral sciences are especially helpful to me in this regard. A large body of data about human behavior, how people learn and change, and how community grows, have become available in the past 20 years. These studies shed light on why people behave as they do; what motivates them, shapes their attitudes, beliefs and value systems; and how they affect one another individually, in groups, in organizations, and in large institutions; and how they enhance or prevent community.[2]

I would like now to explore with you the structure of the local congregation and how its style of leadership affects both the member initiative and the quality of Christian community.

A primary blockage of the local congregation in realizing its potential in community is its continuing the pre-Reformation, Medieval structure of the congregation. The church then understood itself as a hierarchy. More than anything else, the power and positions of its clergy provided its identity. Christian vocation was limited to those who were properly ordained; only then were you a priest and a minister. The laity, it was assumed, did not have a

[2]See Emma Lou Benignus, "The Use of Applied Behavioral Sciences in Clergy Development." *Journal of Religion and the Applied Behavior Sciences*, Vol. 1, No. 1, 1979.

ministry. Indeed, those clergy who had to relate to the laity were known as secular clergy. They had to move between the holiness of the church and the unholiness of the world. It was through the mystery of the clergy's power and ability to consecrate the sacramental elements that the laity drew near to the holiness of God. The people were literally dependent upon the ministry of the clergy in order to obtain grace and salvation. An authoritarian, paternalistic church produced an apathetic, dependent laity who sought and found their community through other means. Spiritual community was found in the monastery or convent, called "religious communities," not available to the masses, to the laity. The priests, the monks, the nuns, alone had Christian vocation.

PRE-REFORMATION MODEL OF THE CHURCH

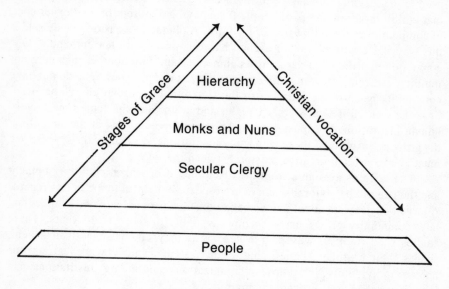

ILLUSTRATION #1

The Reformation stood in condemnation of this church, and on very sound biblical and theological grounds. So has Vatican II. Luther insisted the church should not be a class structure, but a single people, *the laos teu theu*, the People of God. Within the church, God indeed created an important office, the public office of ministry. But, that office could be occupied by anyone among the people who could faithfully speak the Word and lead the people in its common worship. If a hierarchy illustrated the Medieval model of the church, then either a circle or an inverted pyramid illustrates the New Testament Reformation model.

REFORMATION MODEL

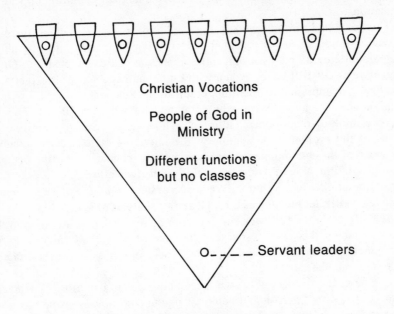

Christian Vocations

People of God in
Ministry

Different functions
but no classes

O_ _/_ _ Servant leaders

ILLUSTRATION #2

While today's church has rubbed off the rough edges of its Medieval
heritage, the authoritarian image remains far too strong, frequently frustrating
the laity's initiative and maintaining a high level of dependency by the parish's
general membership on the professional leadership, especially on the clergy. It
is detrimental to both laity and clergy—detrimental to the whole church. It is a
blockage to fostering a community of self-responsible, yet interdependent persons which more accurately describes the biblical nature of the church. We
need not allow this unhealthy situation to continue. Under the guidance of the
Spirit, we are capable of significantly altering the local parish from its typical
authoritarian, leader-dominated structure to a much more open and supportive
community. Though we may never totally invert the pyramid or eliminate
social structure, we can reduce the social distance between the parish's primary
leadership group and the membership base.

We cannot fault any one person or group. Pastors today, as I relate to
them, do not want to be or appear authoritarian. And, laity are not always sure
what they expect of their pastor in this regard. For good or bad, society, in
general, and the people within the church have a very high expectation of being
involved, in some manner or other, in those decisions that affect them personally. Leaders and membership generally recognize that folks want to be involved in the decision processes. Yet, we still have not always discovered how

to make it happen. And, congregations with the best intentions about total membership participation often, in the end, evaluate their condition far short of expectations.

This week and through the 80s, we need to be as creative and as imaginative, and in doing so, be as practical as Henry Ford's insight into assembling the automobile on a conveyor belt rather than in a stationary position. Or, as imaginative as Dr. Bill Foege, when with Lutheran missionaries in Nigeria, he radicalized the approach to smallpox eradication. Research, insight, courage, commitment and teamwork must be combined for what becomes the "why-didn't-we-think-of-that-sooner" solution. While we will dare to identify components of the problem, the seminary, the laity, the clergy, certain theologies—none of these components dare become a scapegoat, distorting perspectives of a solution. We will stagnate at this point if we allow ourselves to fault one party or another in the church. We need a system approach to the dilemma.

In that spirit, let me take us through a brief analysis of leadership style and its casual effect on the follower's initiative. The research and literature in this field is growing and is a rich resource for our purposes. At the Center for Parish Development, we have made this a primary focus of our work. Several factors should be remembered.

1. One never shapes one's own leadership style in isolation. Whatever it is, it grows on a person and is more often unconsciously shaped by one's experiences in particular organizations and by the culture in general. After a period in a leadership position, many of us have simply settled into a style that, in our generally uncritical judgment, feels good and, from what we can tell, gets the job done. In any case, one's leadership style forms over a period of time. Where an openness to change is present, trust levels are high, and supportive relations are good, the congregational leadership can evolve toward new and perhaps healthier patterns of relationship and decision making. However, an effort on the part of a pastor to alter a leadership style without a mutual understanding with the church's lay leadership, generally ends in disaster. To be sure, the initiative for change should come from the pastor. The lay leadership and the pastor must together understand what they are attempting, and together learn new and appropriate skills for community growth and development.

2. Since leadership is always relational, my style of leadership is not what I, myself, necessarily think it to be. Rather, my leadership style is what my followers perceive me to be as a leader. Follower behavior is significantly determined by their perception of me and my approach, and not by how I perceive myself. This insight is extremely important. Its implications are significant. As a pastor, I may summon the congregation to a new vision and a new program. Then, after a lot of hard work on the part of a few, I become frustrated and even angry when the congregation responds feebly. My gut assumption: "They" are the problem. Indeed, they may be the problem. But, maybe the problem is in the particular style of lead-

ership and its correlated process of decision making in the parish. How people perceive our leadership is a powerful factor in determining the nature of people's responses, though certainly not the only factor.

Clergy, in general, and younger clergy, in particular, would not dare to be thought of as authoritarian. The spirit of our times is such that we prize being open and nonoppressive. Indeed, if there is one characteristic of our day, it is the almost universal expectation that one has a right to be a part of the decision process, that no agency has a right to decide matters on my behalf without at least consulting me in some manner. Generally, we know this. But, our ability to be assertive and strong while still conveying an openness, especially when conditions within the parish are difficult, is not easy. Our studies indicate that many pastors who strongly perceive themselves as being open and receptive to the ideas of others, are seen as oppressive and manipulative, in the eyes of many followers, especially when their value system is threatened.

3. Basic to the Authoritarian style is the need to control the parish. This is a tendency that can be found in both liberal and conservative clergy. The power associated with the office, along with techniques of management are utilized to ''lead'' the parish in a certain direction. Now, this may not be all wrong. But, it does raise the question of ownership. Just whose parish is it? And, what is it in the office of the public ministry, in the education of the pastor, that enables him or her to own in a superior way the direction or the goals of the parish? Of course, many a pastor would respond, as I have often done, ''The membership doesn't appear to care about the church's direction or future; they only object at being faithful.'' But again, we need to see the problem not from a we/they. We need to ask what is really functioning here. Has a particular style of parish leadership (along with other factors) shaped a dependency relationship of the congregation on the pastor, one that predictably breeds apathy and a natural reflex to object to any change that disturbs.

The pressures on the pastor to control the parish come from various sources.[3] Some church bodies and administrative units, more than others, keep the pressure on the pastor. In other cases, the tradition of the parish itself, or an element of its membership, pressures the pastor. Or, the pastor's own value system may be a driving force. In any case, he or she appears to pressure the parish. The result is a molding and shaping of the parish to conform to a specific value system, or to value systems in conflict. In the heat of conflict, and in an effort to succeed, each party coats his or her dominant direction with theological rhetoric, a theology that is not always defensible. In a parish where there is a feeling of control by a few at the top, many members resist, and for the simple fact, they do not feel a part of the parish. The question persists: Whose church is it?

---

[3]Donald P. Smith's book, *Clergy in the Cross Fire,* is a helpful analysis of this pressure-cooker condition of the parish.

The recent study of perspectives on pastoral and congregational effectiveness in Lutheran churches, reported in *Ten Faces of Ministry*, supports the point here being made.[4] Of the five items indicating pastoral effectiveness, Lutherans identified two as strongly negative in effectiveness. Of the two, the strongest "Not Wanted" was Dominating Influence of pastoral leadership. The Brekke study shares my observations that we are focusing on a matter that goes beyond conveying the authority of the Word. The manner and the degree to which pastors go beyond this line, and under what circumstances, may be debated. The point is that a persistently perceived dominating pattern of leadership frustrates lay initiative. And, evidence supports the alternative, the development of a more open, supportive, and collaborative leadership style by the top leadership team (clergy and lay together) can positively affect the member's ownership of the parish's purpose and program.

The seminaries, in my judgment, and many by their own admission, have not yet utilized the training designs available for enabling the local parish to move toward a greater feeling of community through a change in leadership style. The challenge to effect the appropriate change demands not merely an inter-disciplinary approach, but also an inter-church agency approach. Seminary programs of continuing education cannot focus exclusively on the pastor removed from his or her parish. To be responsible to the necessary change process, the seminary and the judicatory need programs of continuing education that literally train the congregational system. The educational process must be both contextual and conjoint. The pastor and the lay leadership of the parish must together examine their leadership and the congregation's decision making process in the context of their congregation. Then through an action-research process move toward new organizational behavior. This is happening in some parts of the country. The training designs are now available. We need carefully-monitored pilot congregations working with seminaries and church officialdom to learn how to reshape the parish toward greater Christian community. This is not an effort to move the local parish from "institution" to "church." We are about the task of altering the parish in its tendency to be authoritarian and controlling toward an institution that is more open, free, intersupportive, while clearly, strongly identifying itself as Christ's community of faith.

Let me now focus on practices that persist without theological foundation, which tend to perpetuate the authoritarian position of the pastor at the expense of good community.

One is identifying the clergy with a divine call at the expense of the common calling of every Christian through baptism. Laity have too often been given the impression or improperly formed the impression that only clergy have a call from God for ministry. Regardless how the misinformation has been conveyed, it is a component to the problem, fostering a hierarchical image of

[4]Milo L. Brekke, Merton P. Strommen, and Dorothy L. Williams, *Ten Faces of Ministry* (Minneapolis: Augsburg, 1979).

84

the church and leading to the laity's dependency relationship to the profession-al.

The only "calling" the Christian knows is the call of the Gospel. The word "calling" in the New Testament never refers to the clergy. In fact, the New Testament does not even know the concept of a clergy class, let alone any sense of a special group in the church having a call from God different from any other person in the church. "Calling" in Scripture always refers to the call of God through His Church to be a Christian.[5]

And, God calls his people to faithfulness in and through their varied vocations, including clergy. The Coonoor Conference saw the implications for this. Healing through the church could not be understood as the role only of the professional, pastor, or medical doctor, but as Tom Droege reported:

> The ministry of healing belongs to the whole congregation. Not just pastor, medical and social worker, sick visitor, or other church officers, but all Christians are called to serve one another and to apply the resources God has provided for the healing of the nations. . . . therefore, members of the congregation will have to be prepared and equipped for their day-to-day ministries, their mission in the world.[6]

The parish must be a place where Christians are spiritually supporting and training each other for both a corporate ministry through their common community and through their many vocations as parent, student, laborer, nurse, teacher—whatever the vocation. In such a parish, we bring together our joys, hurts, and needs known at the center of our lives. We share and support each other humanly and warmly because we are helped and can help each other in Christ. In this way, the congregation grows as community.

Too often the laity's summons for service is in the form of a supportive role to the maintenance of the parish organization. We cannot belittle such calls for service. The problem is that such service to the organization is gener-ally the limit of acknowledgement of the laity's ministry and service. Out-standing, however, should be the image of the laity carrying on many and varied ministries in the home, society, and vocation. Service in and through the local parish should be seen as supportive to this multiple ministry. This accent needs at least to balance the service roles of the parish as a corporate body.

The seminary may theologically educate the future pastor for this type of parish. Unfortunately, it tends to do so with superficial relations to the laity, seldom in the context of their vocations.[7]

A related item is ordination. The misunderstanding or perhaps misuse of ordination is another factor contributing to the sense of hierarchy, inhibiting

---

[5]The one possible exception, 1 Cor. 7:20, is unclear and the subject of different interpretations by scholars.

[6]*That Thy Saving Health May Be Known*, Concordia Theological Monthly, Occasional Papers No. 2, May, 1968.

[7]The Laity Project, led by Richard Broholm and Gabriel Fackre at Andover Newton Theological Seminary, Andover, Mass., is an example of a seminary working with itself and with congrega-tions in an effort to move beyond the model of ministry in an exclusive sense.

community. Certainly, ordination has a legitimate purpose in the life of the church. Properly trained persons are needed in order to function publicly on behalf of the local congregation. As individuals, they need to be legitimated— there needs to be public symbols, indicating who they are, what public responsibilities they have, and who authorizes them to function publicly on the church's behalf. Ordination is necessary and important for the public life of the church.

However, we must also examine the effect some of the symbols of ordination have upon the church in regard to community development. Have you ever surveyed or interviewed worshippers following an ordination or an installation service? Having observed the laying on of hands by the neighboring clergy and the ecclesiastical officialdom, the impression is powerfully given. This person is being inducted into the local clergy fraternity and is given strange powers in order to carry on his or her ministry among us. Seldom have the symbols around ordination given an image of the common ministries of the congregational membership, that the pastor is being set aside to publicly lead the community in its common and varied ministries. There are too few symbols depicting the servant role of the public office.

We clergy have not always been clear among ourselves as to what we have received in our theological education, and in our ordination that is both to be expected and also to be found in the laity. The manner of utilizing our theological education may actually perpetuate the laity's dependency, one that frustrates achieving interdependency necessary for a healthy community life. Having studied long and hard, and therefore perceiving ideas of what the church should be, as a clergy person, I may be quick to talk, slow to listen, impatient while others struggle through a matter, and feel intolerant when others arrive at a different conclusion than I. Then, of course, there is also that frequently heard lay voice, difficult for the pastor to manage, "Pastor, tell us the Bible answer—you're the one theologically trained."

Fewer and fewer lay people are allowing themselves to be dependent upon an authority figure. It was one thing to look to the clergy person and the physician for answers to every human problem, when they were the only educated persons in the town. Times have changed. And, here I suspect clergy may share a professional problem similar to that now being experienced by the medical obstetrician. To illustrate my point, let me venture into another's field and do so with considerable uneasiness.

For thousands of years, women have been training each other in the art of child-bearing. Only within the past 75 years have they become dependent upon professionals in order to have their babies. Ironically, with the advancement of obstetrical science, and the growing expertise of the medical doctor, women came to know less than ever before about themselves. Childbirth historically was a communal affair. The women of the village, the mother and the midwife, worked as a team, to assure a healthy birth.[8] But, as childbirth moved

[8]See Richard W. Wertz and Dorothy C. Wertz, *Lying-In: A History of Childbirth in America* (New York: Free Press, 1977).

86

into the hospital under professional medicine, it became a very private matter between doctor and mother, with father and all others excluded from the process. Once the mother had assigned herself to the physician, there was little for her to do in preparation for the delivery. The professionals would take charge of everything. She needed only to know the signs of labor in order to call the doctor to take over. Asleep through the delivery, the mother could be given her baby a day later. In the meantime, the father stood outside the whole affair, depicted in the cartoons as a dumb, anxious chainsmoker.

During the past 25 years, there has been a quiet, but steady movement of women challenging the dominant role of the physician in the childbirth process. Women began educating women on alternate, parent-centered approaches to delivery. Separate movements began within the childbirth movement; for instance, the formation of mothers supporting mothers in the art of breast-feeding, a practice that the professional generally had come to discourage.

With new knowledge and greater self-confidence through mutual support, mothers began talking with the physician regarding their own expectations about the birthing process. The reaction of many of the obstetrical physicians to this new assertive patient is interesting to study. Doctors who had become accustomed to an authoritarian, dominant role in their practice easily became offended, threatened, and in many cases, hostile. Those doctors not threatened and willing to examine change within their health care system accepted the fact that women have something significant to share with the professional, and are capable of doing many things well which modern technology and scientific practices cannot. And, indeed, best of all, there could be recognition that women were being responsible for themselves. In such cases, the doctor may painfully reexamine his or her role in order to support parents and not adversely control the process.

However, the change of role and authority on the part of the obstetrical physician is not without stress and conflict, as I observe the scene. Where a mutual change process is not negotiated openly between the physician and the woman, conclusions are made and practices begun that may ultimately be detrimental to both parties. Doctors bringing lawsuits against mid-wives; doctors censoring doctors who cooperate with parents wanting home births; and women/parents practicing home births with limited health care. A current issue of *OMNI* magazine paints a frightening picture of how this tension and conflict could degenerate, if unresolved.

The analogy to the church can be more sharply drawn. What an ideal situation for change. The doctor, the nurse, the mid-wife, the father, and the mother, mutually working together as a team to assure the optimum birthing process, a community, each with special gifts to be shared, to assure new life. And the church? The pastor, the doctor, the counselor, the social worker, the mother, the father, student, men, women, and children in all sorts and conditions of life, functioning as a team through the local congregation, mutually supporting each other and the parish through many and varied ministries. Each

87

assisting the other to discover the gifts of God that disclose the possibilities of ministry as human needs are identified.

While the conflict and tension may not be as dramatic in the church as in the O.B./childbirth movement, there are similarities. The mainline congregations are poorly relating to a powerful religious movement in our day. People are generally looking for their spiritual fulfillment in other places. Several factors are frequently evident. People cannot find meaningful community or cooperative support for their emerging or changed values in our parishes. Or, they chafe under what they perceive to be authoritarian and oppressive conditions within our congregations. In many cases because we cannot be the attracting community we should be, the religious movement has taken shape in house churches, small neighborhood Bible study groups, prayer groups in industrial settings, and perhaps most of all, before the T.V.

Like the home-birth delivery that certainly will suffer ultimately if it is denied or denies itself the resources of modern medicine, so the privatized, "do-it-yourself," anti-institutional expressions of "church" will suffer in isolation from the competencies of the church's historical, theological resources. But, just as the obstetrical doctor will suffer by an inability to alter his or her role in practice, ultimately denying the possibility of optimum health care through a self-responsible client system, so also, the church and its clergy will miss a unique opportunity to restructure the practice of faith to be more fully the People of God, knowing and practicing as a community the forgiveness of sins, the healing process, and celebrating life in the midst of death, in sharing the hope of the resurrection, the ultimate health.

Dr. Sharon Telleen

CHAPTER VI

The Church as a Support to Families Under Stress

by Sharon Telleen

This paper will examine the family's strengths and stresses from the social psychological perspective. The strengths of families will be defined as they relate to the changing composition of the American family, the characteristics of healthy family functioning, and the supports families use to manage the stress of daily strains, crises, and life transitions.

The research literature on family functioning, stress, and support provide a starting point for more fully developing the Church's role as a support to families. The findings presented here can be used as a conceptual framework to produce models and implement approaches at the parish level.

Questions arise concerning the family's ability to remain healthy and fully functional in the presence of the stresses families encounter today. To address this issue it is necessary to examine the characteristics which social psychologists have used to define a healthy family. How has the healthy family typically dealt with the stresses of role changes and the stress of crises and transitions? What supports do families say are most helpful and needed? An examination of the ways the healthy family deals with stress and heals itself can provide a normative guide for the health and healing process in families.

Although healthy families cope by becoming self-sufficient and relying on inner resources, they are also closely tied to the larger community for support in this function. We will explore the supports that the community and social institutions can provide and that the family finds most useful.

The Church is an institution that can directly support families. It has the potential of continued contact across generations and throughout the individual's lifespan. What impact does this institution have on the family? What support is it presently giving to families and what can it do in the future to more effectively help families? This paper will address these and related issues.

Profile of the Changing American Family

The composition of the American family is changing. The typical nuclear family of mother, father, and children with one income now accounts for only 13% of all U.S. households. One of the changes has been the increase in women in the work force, particularly married women with children (dual breadwinner nuclear family). According to a report of the U.S. Bureau of Labor Statistics released in 1977 (Table 1), dual breadwinner nuclear families comprise 16% of the households in the U.S. One-third of all employed women have children under 18 years of age. The projections through 1990 are for continued growth in the female labor force. The number of working mothers with children under the age of six is expected to increase by 56% of the 1978 level. By 1980 there will be an increase of 3.1 million working mothers with young children. The number of working mothers with children between six and 17 is also expected to increase 56% over the 1978 level, an increase of 5.5 million women. By 1990 nearly 10.5 million children may have working mothers, (Moore, 1979).

Table 1

Family Strengths

ADULT DISTRIBUTION IN U.S. HOUSEHOLDS: 1975

Single-parent families	16%
Single, widowed, separated, or divorced persons	21%
Childfree or postchild marriages	23%
Dual breadwinner nuclear families	16%
Single breadwinner nuclear families	13%
No breadwinner nuclear families	1%
Extended families	6%
Experimental families or cohabiting	4%
	100%

Bureau of Labor Statistics. *News Release.* USDL 77-191 March 8, 1977.

A second factor affecting the American family is the increase in families headed by women. Over the past ten years families headed by women have grown nearly ten times faster than mother-father families. The increase is due primarily to the increasing incidence of divorce, births to adolescents, and to an increasing tendency for women to establish households independent of relatives, (Snapper and Ohms, 1977). In 1977 more than half of all female family heads were in the work force, (Moore, 1979).

These two factors are part of a "subtle revolution" and will have a substantial impact on the way children are raised, the role of the father, the division of labor in the household, and the use of time, (Smith, 1979). They also create what Pearlin and Schooler (1978) have termed "persistent life strains," stresses that are related to one's role and the functions necessary for that role. The increase in single parent families also means that more families are facing the crises of bereavement, divorce, or separation and the relatively long transition state of adjusting to widowhood or single parenting. These must

92

be added to the acute crises families have traditionally dealt with—disaster, war, prolonged separation due to job, illness, and death.

The Church can do much to alleviate the stress associated with these changes. However, before examining the Church's role it is necessary to look at the family, determine how it effectively deals with these stresses of crisis and transition, and to examine the types of support the family finds most helpful.

Characteristics of Healthy Family Functioning

There are many definitions of the healthy family. Characteristics of healthy family functioning have been identified by psychiatrists, social psychologists, sociologists, and anthropologists. It is necessary to provide a working synthesis of these definitions. Barnhill (1979) reviewed the literature that attempted to define healthy families. He identified four major themes in healthy family functioning: Identity Processes, Change, Information Processing, and Role Structuring. Within each of these categories are two dimensions. (See Table 2).

Table 2

The Healthy Family System

Themes	Dimensions
IDENTITY PROCESSES	1. Individuation vs. Enmeshment A firm sense of autonomy, personal responsibility, identity and boundaries of the self, "has faith in his own competence, appreciates his own worth." 2. Mutuality vs. Isolation A sense of emotional closeness or intimacy
CHANGE	3. Flexibility vs. Rigidity The capacity to be adjustable and resilient in response to varied conditions and the process of change—nonstereotyped and repetitive responses. 4. Stability vs. Disorganization Consistency, responsibility, and security in family interactions.
INFORMATION PROCESSING	5. Clear vs. Distorted Perception A consensual validation of events by family members. 6. Clear vs. Distorted Communication Clarifying meaning and intent of communications among family members.
ROLE STRUCTURING	7. Role Reciprocity vs. Role Conflict Mutually agreed roles in which an individual complements the role of the partner. Each fulfills the needs of the other. 8. Clear Generational vs. Diffuse Generational Boundaries Specific types of role reciprocity; parent-child, sibling-sibling.

Adapted from Barnhill, "Healthy Family Systems." *Family Coordinator*, January, 1979.

He emphasizes that these dimensions are interrelated. If one dimension is changed it affects family behavior in another. For instance, development of clear communication between family members will lead to trust (mutuality) and to clearer perceptions of family members. Clear communication also facilitates role reciprocity.

Gerald Caplan in his work with families in community settings has emphasized two of these dimensions in particular—mutuality and reciprocity, (Caplan and Killilea, 1976). Mutuality and reciprocity ensure that each family member not only guides but receives guidance. Each time a person in the family aids another there are as many benefits for the giver as for the recipient. Mutuality and reciprocity must be developed through enhanced communication and clear perceptions of family members.

The Healthy Family and Life Stress

Stress is the major threat to healthy family functioning, both physically and as a social system. There has been extensive investigation recently linking stress and psychiatric and physical illness, (Dean and Lin, 1977). The family must keep stress within manageable bounds if it is to stay healthy.

Stress can be precipitated by life events such as the death of a spouse, a job change or a move. A number of life-event scales have been developed to measure these stressful events.

Three major types of stressful life events can be identified in the research literature: 1) persistent life strains or deficits; 2) crises; and 3) transitions. Pearlin and Schooler (1978:3) have defined persistent life strains as those enduring problems one faces in the social roles of parent, spouse, and breadwinner. They are the stressors associated with the everyday pursuit of one's activities. If one is operating in a deficit situation, without the aid of a spouse or financial resources, the strains one experiences may be greater, (Weiss, 1976).

Crises are acute "severely upsetting situations of limited duration in which an individual's resources must be hastily summoned to cope with threats to his or her emotional stability," (Weiss, 1974:214).

Life cycle transitions are the adjustments after a crisis—the adjustment to widowhood, to parenthood, or to marital separation. Such a transition is "characterized by disruption of preexisting social equilibria. . . . The transition state ends with the establishment of a new stable life organization accompanied by a new stable identity," (Weiss, 1974:214).

There is a growing body of literature linking stressful life events to illness. High scores on life events scales have been related to psychiatric symptoms, physical indices of psychiatric illnesses, depression, suicide attempts, heart disease and leukemia, (Dean and Lin, 1977). In a recent study, Haynes (1980) reported that working per se will not put women at greater risk of heart disease, but working at a clerical job while being the mother of young children does put a woman at greater risk. For working women, as the number of children rises, the incidence of heart trouble rises.

Although there appears to be a relationship between stressful life events and illness, the event itself accounts for less than 10% of the variance in the onset of illness. Further, the predictive power of the life event scale is limited, (Lin, Ensel, Simeone and Kuo, 1979). While there is common situational distress (the same situation produced similar behavior in different individuals such as the stages of grief in the loss of a spouse, facing one's own death, the loss of a child), the outcome—illness or adjustment—is related to a number of factors other than the stressful event. Colletta (1979), in a study of recently divorced mothers found that the amount of stress varied depending on level of income, institutional and familial support, and the psychological resources of the individual.

These mediating factors may mean the difference between poor outcome and keeping the family healthy and intact during a stressful event. Empirical research has identified a number of mediating factors important in handling stress. Five of these are: 1) family resources—personality traits of individual family members and the characteristics of the family unit; 2) personal belief systems, including religious beliefs; 3) emotional mastery, management of individual anxiety; 4) coping response styles of direct attack on the stressor event or related stressors; and 5) support systems within the family and community.

Factors Mediating Stressful Events

Family Resources. Family resources are those inherent characteristics of the family that make it more likely that the family will use coping behavior. Hill and Hansen (1962) studied families facing various disasters—both natural and man-made. They found that the chance of adaptive coping behavior is more likely in those families that fit Barnhill's definition of a healthy family. Adaptive behavior was more likely in families that 1) were intact and well-integrated; 2) had open channels of communication; 3) exhibited flexible authority and status structures; and 4) had successfully met past disasters. Caplan (1976) found similar characteristics of families that effectively coped with the loss of a relative in the Yom Kippur War. Characteristics of individual family members also contribute to the effective handling of stress. Pearlin and Schooler (1978) found that the personality characteristics of adequate self-esteem and a sense of mastery were important for dealing effectively with persistent life strains.

Religious Beliefs. Research on family functioning has reported a positive relationship of religious orientation to marital happiness and successful family relationships, (Stinnet, 1979; Beam, 1979). Many families reported that they had an "awareness of God or a higher power that gave them a sense of purpose and gave their family a sense of support and strength," (Stinnett, 1979;27).

McCubbin (1979) studied the coping responses of families experiencing family separation in one of three conditions: 1) regular, one week separation related to job (minimal stress); 2) regular 8-month separation for naval sea duty (moderate stress); and 3) prolonged separation of six years for families of

96

prisoners of war or soldiers missing in action (severe stress). Families reported that religious beliefs were one of the most important factors in their ability to manage the stress of separation, particularly for those experiencing moderate and severe stress.

Spiritual support is helpful because among other positive effects it helps maintain the family unit, contributes to individual self-esteem through love and care, and serves as a reference point for norms, values, and expectations which may guide families in stressful situations. Perhaps another reason is that religious values share the same characteristics of healthy families. Norquist (1979) in a study of the biblical view of the family reported that there was a democratization of the family in the New Testament, even a "mutual subordination." According to biblical interpretation, whatever the structure (composition) of the family, role definition needs to be carried out with mutuality, intimacy, cooperation, and love and concern. These, of course, are some of the characteristics of a supportive, healthy family.

In addition, the rituals generally associated with religious beliefs are helpful to the family. The regular weekly liturgy is considered extremely important to the health of many parishioners in that it provides continual social contact and a sense of regularity and order, (R. Caplan, 1972). The regular social contact provides an informal social network from which a support system can emerge.

Emotional Mastery. Hansen and Johnson (1979) in a discussion of family stresses state that two elements that produce stress are a rapid rate of change and the uncertainty and ambiguity that accompanies change. The effects of the rate of change modified if the individual perceives the change to be desirable or under control. The ambiguities introduced by the change create individual anxiety. Managing anxiety is one of the coping responses that is most effective in dealing with stress, (McCubbin, 1979). Caplan (1976) in his work during the Yom Kippur War reported that families required a great deal of energy to manage the anxiety of the sitution.

The Church and family members can provide support in emotional mastery and in the reduction of anxiety. The Church's use of prayer and meditation allows one to relax, gather inner resources, and think more clearly. Support and feedback from the family network and a community support group also aid in reducing anxiety. Caplan recounts many instances during the Yom Kippur War in which family members, through the support of family and community, were able to keep their emotions in check and turn to the more active coping responses that alleviate stressful situations. The Church can also provide the presence of others. The powerful impact of the presence and touch of another can have a calming effect and alleviate stress, (Lynch, 1977).

Coping Responses. Coping responses vary in effectiveness depending on the nature of the stress. With respect to the stress accompanying the crisis of separation, McCubbin (1979) found that the coping strategies common to all families were: 1) establishing independence; and 2) increasing self-sufficiency. In many instances wives learned to manage finances and worked to attain the additional skills they would need to manage the family alone.

Colletta (1979) found similar results among divorced members. She reported that moderate income, divorced mothers were generally satisfied with the level of support received even though it was less than that received by low income mothers. These mothers reported using an active coping strategy in their transition to single parenting and appreciated their sense of independence and ability to make decisions.

For other families undergoing minimal and moderate stress, there was the value of building and maintaining supportive relationships between family members and persons in the community. They were also better able to cope with stress if they perceived their behavior as consistent with the norms and expectations of the business or military organization they were associated with, (McCubbin, 1979).

In the stress accompanying persistent life strains of marriage and parenting, Pearlin and Schooler (1978) found that the possession of certain personality characteristics such as a sense of control and adequate self-esteem is not as important as the actual use of coping responses. "It is the specific things that people do in dealing with life strains that determine most closely whether or not they will experience emotional distress," (Pearlin and Schooler, 1978:4).

Which coping responses are most helpful in alleviating persistent life strains? Pearlin found that self-reliance was most effective in reducing stress. An active coping strategy of managing the situation and gaining some control was effective. Beyond self-reliance, the other coping strategies of selective ignoring or negotiating were equally effective. However, the most effective copers were those who used the full range of coping responses available, not just one or two. In coping with moderate to severe stress, families not only spent considerable effort to maintain family integration and stability but also sought to maintain ties with relatives and in-laws. Wives also became involved with other wives in collective group activities designed to seek some resolution to the stressful situation. This included the development of close interpersonal relationships with wives in similar crisis situations. Through collective efforts family members were able to obtain partial control over the situation and reduce the impact of stress on the family.

Support Systems. Social support is considered an important moderator of life stress. According to Lin et al. (1979:109), "social support may be defined as support accessible to an individual through social ties to other individuals, groups and the large community. The general assumption is that social support is negatively related to illness. The greater the social support that an individual receives, in the form of supportive relationships with family members, kin, friends, acquaintances, co-workers and the larger community, the less likely that the individual will experience illness."

Caplan has defined the functions of a support system as 1) helping the individual exposed to stress to mobilize his psychological resources and master his emotional burdens; 2) sharing his tasks in dealing concretely with his predicament; and 3) providing him with extra supplies of information, money and materials, tools, skills, and cognitive guidance to improve his handling of the situation, (Caplan and Killilea, 1976:5).

There are two major sources of support: individual support (including family members) and community support (from an informal network of friends or from institutions). Support from family members plays an important role in reducing the likelihood of stress and the onset of illness. McCubbin (1979) found that among the most effective coping strategies for families undergoing moderate to severe stress was the ability to maintain family ties and family integrity, integration, and stability. Clearly, people looked to family members to provide support in times of crisis and spent energy to keep those ties operating.

Colletta (1979) reported that recently divorced mothers across all income levels received the most assistance from family rather than friends or neighbors. A large majority (83 percent) of low-income single parent families and 66 percent of the moderate income single parent families were assisted by their families.

Lee (1979) reported that family members were most helpful in long-term enduring crises while friends and neighbors were more helpful in acute short-term situations. Individuals look first to their family and kin for support before going to the community, (Uzoka, 1979). Other researchers have also pointed to the supportive function of the family, (Sussman, 1979; Sussman and Bruchinal, 1962; and Uzoka, 1979). Although the family of mother, father, and young children generally live in separate and sometimes distant households from relatives and other kin, they remain active participants in the primary kin network. The family still operates as an extended family. There is mutual financial aid among kin; kin are looked to for support during events such as weddings or crises such as death, accident, or natural disaster.

Caplan has identified nine ways in which the healthy family supports its members, (Caplan and Killilea, 1976:5). These supports also facilitate some of the emotional mastery and coping strategies that enable individuals to deal with stress. It is important that those working with families be aware of the supports that Caplan has identified. Knowledge of the supports family members give one another allow the helper to identify and supplement the supports that the family members cannot give during a crisis. It also allows community groups to use these nine supports as a model for planning their own supports to families in stress.

1. *The Family as a Collector and Disseminator of Information.* Multigenerational learnings are possible in both directions, from young to old and old to young.

2. *The Family as a Feedback Guidance System.* Family members can help one another make valid assessments of their behavior in new situations by giving reactions.

3. *The Family as a Source of Ideology.* The family provides belief systems, value systems and codes of behavior that are expected of its members. These traditions offer a source of guidance and support during time of crisis.

4. *The Family as a Guide and Mediator in Problem Solving.* The family acts to guide each other in dealing with a problem and finding external sources of care and assistance. The family benefits from the input and experiences of many generations.

5. *The Family as a Source of Practical Service and Concrete Aid.* Mutual aid among family members in the form of money, gifts, and help with household tasks is an important source of support during crisis and periods of transition when the individual is so preoccupied with the crisis. Because it is a natural part of family living, the recipient can maintain his own autonomy.

6. *The Family as a Haven for Rest and Recuperation.* The family legitimizes the need for rest so the individual has a chance to collect his thoughts in order to resume control of the crisis without feeling he has lost control while resting.

7. *The Family as a Reference and Control Group.* As a reference group the family does not judge. As a control group it rewards successes in adhering to the family code and punishes failures, with the full knowledge that their destinies are bound together and they continue to accept one another for what they are.

8. *The Family as a Source and Validator of Identity.* During a crisis of transition one can become uncertain about his identity, strengths, ability, etc. The family supports the individual by reminding him of past and present successes.

9. *The Family as a Contributor to Emotional Mastery.* The family can aid the individual in devoting his energy toward grappling constructively with the problem and controlling his feelings of despair and helplessness by their continual presence.

Support from family members clearly plays an important role in reducing the likelihood of stress and the onset of illness. However, research evidence suggests that such support may also be effectively provided through a person's ties to extrafamilial individuals and groups. Nuckolls, Cassel and Kaplan (1972) report that pregnant women who experienced many stressful life events and low support scores (low quality of marital relationships, interaction with extended family, and adjustment within community) had a much higher rate of pregnancy complications than those women who also experienced many stressful life events but scored high on the social support scale.

McCubbin's study of families under stress identified three major reasons why the community can be an effective support system:

> 1) it provides norms and expectations of how families can best manage events; 2) in cooperation with family members, the community offers social support through interpersonal relationships; and 3) it provides the context in which families may unite in a collective effort to deal directly with the stressor event, (McCubbin, 1979:244).

The Church as Support to Families

Through the interaction of the family unit and the community, the family is better able to manage stress. The church is one of the institutions within the community that individuals can rely on for support. The social science research on the relation between the church and families has concentrated almost exclusively on the relation between religious beliefs and a strong and healthy family. The influence of the church as a support in other areas has been less thoroughly researched. Therefore, it is necessary to use other models and research as a guide. The research on the ways family members and other institutions support one another in crisis provides guidelines for ways the church can support the family.

In discussing the church as a support to families, this paper will concentrate on the role of the parish. The parish has great potential as a support to families. One reason is that the parish considers the family to be one of its ministries. Norquist (1979), a theologian at the Lutheran School of Theology in Chicago, in a survey of the biblical treatment of the family, pointed out that the ministry of the church is to assist and support families in their secular function as well as to assist them in worship and the teaching of religion. National church body statements on marriage and the family have also advocated that the church minister to families.

In addition to biblical and organizational sanction to minister to families, the parish is organized in a way in which it can serve as a support to families. It has the potential for personal contact with an individual throughout his life-span. The parish is usually a multi-generational network, including both old and young, and this gives perspective to the guidance it can offer.

Among the moderators of life stress, there are three that have particular significance for the parish: a religious belief system, emotional mastery and a social support network. The first is presently built into the life of the parish through pastoral supports, Bible study, religious education programs, and worship services. The second is also contained within the church through the activities of prayer, meditation, and pastoral contact. These traditional ministries of the church need to be recognized for their tremendous potential for healing.

A third moderator of stress, availability of a social support system, will be examined here in more detail. The idea of the parish as a social support system for families is not new. It has been advocated by church leaders and organizations. Robert Marshall, past president of the Lutheran Church in America,

101

wrote in a communication to all pastors of the LCA on May 1, 1974:

> The church can still be a strong support system for the family. It can show how family life needs to be worked at. It can demonstrate the dynamics that build companionships. It can knock on the door and get into the home with a fair chance of being welcome. The church can draw families together at the altar. It can reconcile, console, and heal when there are troubles and break-downs. It can care.

Use of the Church as a Support. The church is used by its members for support in times of stress. McCubbin (1979) found that families under moderate and severe stress turned to the church for support. Colletta (1979) in a study of divorced mothers found that the church was mentioned as one of the institutions used for support. One mother said, "We're also very active in the church; we go every Sunday. Brian goes to Sunday School. The weekends I'm off I help with the teen groups. Church is a good place for me to get together and make friends."

However, only three of the 72 families interviewed indicated they had used the church even though many more than that claimed a religious preference. There was one each from the 24 moderate income one-parent families, from the 24 low income families and from the 24 moderate income two-parent families. There were no differences in the use of the church among families of varying incomes and number of parents present. In contrast, the most commonly used services were those that were directly related to the health and care of children: day care subsidy, medical clinics, family and children's services.

Further, questions still remain regarding the types of support people most frequently use the church for, the percent of members who use the church as a support and the use, if any, by individuals other than members. There are also questions concerning the types of support the family would find most helpful.

There are two major ways in which the parish has served as a support system for families: 1) an organized support system consisting of self-help and support groups; and 2) an informal, supportive network.

The Parish as an Organized Support System. The church can provide support to families through the use of organized social support groups. Marie Killilea (1976:78) identified four major categories of organized self-help groups: 1) groups that help in a crisis or transition (Widow-to-Widow, Parents Without Partners); 2) groups that help people with a permanent, stigmatized condition (dwarfs, ex-convicts, homosexuals); 3) groups that help people trapped in a habit and who want a behavioral change (Weight Watchers, Alcoholics Anonymous); and 4) groups that provide personal growth and self-improvement (prayer groups, the Koinonia Group).

The organized groups most frequently found in churches are the first and last—groups that help with a crisis and personal growth groups. There are other organized support groups that have been proposed by the Lutheran Church Women of the LCA (Daehling, 1977). They would constitute a fifth category: support groups for the helpers (Support Groups for Ministry in the Community, Referral Groups, and Advocacy Groups). The guidelines established by the

Lutheran Church Women for the development of support groups deserve further attention and action. They would provide an excellent starting point for model building and implementation of support groups in congregations. In addition, the Episcopal Church has developed an effective support system for clergy, that has been extremely successful. Its approach could be adapted for the parish generally, (Caplan and Killilea, 1976).

The Parish as an Informal Support System

The use of an informal social network as a support requires the parish to look at itself in a slightly different way. An informal or natural social network involves those individuals with whom a person is in contact on a regular basis, (Speck and Attneave, 1973). Within any social network there are individuals who serve a supportive function and others who do not and may even be disliked. From the social network of the individual and the family come the potential helpers and supporters for that family. The parish is part of the church member's natural social network. It therefore can serve as a source of support for individuals in that network.

As a caring social network the parish can assume many of the functions of a support system, (Caplan, 1976). It can:

1) help the individual master his emotional burdens through prayer, meditation, and social contact,

2) share the tasks that need to be done to deal with a crisis, such as providing transportation, doing the shopping, making necessary phone calls, and

3) provide extra supplies of information, money, materials, tools, skills, and cognitive guidance.

As the professional leader of this caring network, the minister is in an excellent position to intervene in a stressful situation, (Caplan, R., 1972). The Harvard Lab of Community Psychiatry in a study of the pastoral practice of home visits found that such visits were extremely successful in providing support to newly widowed persons. They were more helpful than a 50-minute counseling session in the minister's office.

The minister has a number of other advantages, (Caplan, 1972). His knowledge of individual members of the congregation enables him to approach a problem more directly and assess its seriousness. His flexible time schedule enables him to reach someone in acute distress quickly. He has a greater chance of seeing people at an early stage of their crisis—at a time when a relatively small amount of intervention and support can make a major difference. Often, he is allowed to intervene when other mental health professionals are not, and he can offer intermittent care over long periods of time. He can serve as an effective problem solver because he is in a position of authority.

This paper will now examine both types of social support, informal and organized, as they could offer support during three types of stressful events—acute crisis, transition states, and persistent strains. This discussion will not attempt to be a comprehensive review of the ways the church has or can be supportive but will provide illustrative examples.

Acute Crisis. The type of support must vary depending on the stress the family is experiencing. For an acute stress or crisis that requires prompt action, the minister may be required to mobilize a support group quickly. A number of intervention models could be used. The strategy that works in one crisis cannot generally be transferred to another without modification. In addition, the church cannot borrow the guidelines used by mental health professionals without modifying them to fit the needs of the church.

One example to study is the crisis intervention used when families in Israel received word that a family member had died or was captured in war. These can be adapted into guidelines that a minister could use to mobilize the informal social network to aid a family in crisis. The following steps were identified, (Caplan, 1976:275):

1. *Convene and link.* Identify the social network of the particular family (friends in the congregation, neighbors, and the larger community) and link the family to this network.
   a. Offer emotional support, cognitive guidance, and concrete help with crisis-related tasks.
   b. Link with dyads—one other person or family who is known and liked by the family and who has experienced the same crisis. Dyads work best in the early days of the crisis.

2. *Maintain a "watching brief."* Initially people turn to their families for support; they want privacy. Be prepared to supplement the family with those individuals in the social network in case there is a call for help.

3. *Avoid labeling and dependency.* Self-esteem is essential to coping with stress. Putting someone in a dependency situation where he/she cannot reciprocate will not enhance self-esteem. Individuals in a crisis need a feeling of pride, autonomy, and the respect of others if they are to effectively cope. Enhance feelings of reciprocity, "we're all in this together."

4. *Move from a passive to an active coping pattern of behavior.* In an acute crisis there is a period of withdrawal to reassess the situation. However, this should not become social isolation. Have those facing the crisis join forces with others experiencing a similar loss so they can be helpers, after the first few weeks. Expose the family to role models who are actively coping.

Transition State. For a lengthy crisis or a transition state such as adjustment to single parenting, widowhood, separation, or divorce, the parish needs to provide different types of support. The amount of support and acceptance usually accorded the individual can vary with the social acceptance of the stress. For instance, the stress of widowhood is more frequently supported than the stress accompanying marital separation or divorce, or the stress of having a teenage parent in the family. One divorced mother interviewed by Colletta (1979) said, ". . . and my family wasn't any help. They're very . . . religious and thought a divorce, no matter how unhappy you are, is a terrible sin. So, all I got from them was preaching."

For individuals in a transition state there needs to be continued support over a long period of time. One of the ways this could be done is to utilize an already existing social network and suggest contact with those in similar life situations. However, this should be done naturally and at the initiation of the people involved. The church needs to be ready with guidelines and resources that people know are available if they choose to use them. Edythe Daehling (personal communication, January 1980) reports one way this can happen.

> Two women from a Lutheran Church Women's group came into my office in November 1979. They said they had formed an LCW as a support group because of their own needs. They wanted help in moving the group along. When I agreed to come and meet with them they told me that the two of them plus one other woman had terminal cancer and wanted to use what time they had left in "supporting others."

In addition to emotional support, the church can provide support with daily life tasks such as shopping and child care. Help in these concrete areas is an important moderator of life stress. One widow whose husband died of cancer when her children were 6 months and 3½ years, said that in the time after her husband's death one of the most supportive acts was offers to watch both children for an afternoon or a day. That was the kind of concrete support she needed and yet it was one of the least frequently offered. In the study by Colletta (1979) one recently divorced mother of young children said, "The church helps me be a better person but it doesn't help me raise my children." Most single parents interviewed turned to other institutions that provided emotional or physical support in raising their children.

A Methodist church in Arlington, Virginia, with a declining membership was assessing the direction of its ministry. It noted that many single mothers and fathers lived in the twenty-story apartment buildings surrounding the church. The congregation decided to approach these parents with information that the church had a Sunday School, and that on one weekday a Boy Scout group met at the church. Ministering to single parents became a primary focus, and the church actively provided the supports that working single parents most needed. When the parents joined the church and thus met other single parents a number of cooperative arrangements developed, including the organization of after school activities at the church. In that particular neighborhood no other community service could have been quite as effective in supporting the single parents.

105

Life Strains. For those families that are healthy and functioning, such as those experiencing the everyday strains of parenting or running a household where both parents work, a different effort is necessary.

First, the church needs to examine its own parish organization to determine that it is not producing additional strains on the family by, for example, holding meetings during the dinner hour, scheduling numerous organizational and committee meetings. For these families, a highly scheduled program for families may be harmful. Instead, intimate, periodic contact with one or two other families in a similar life situation could be more supportive.

Families in a similar life situation may want to join forces to tackle common problems. The World Council of Churches has developed a Family Power Program. An example of its success is that within congregations in Madras, India, families worked together to solve common problems of obtaining medical care and loans, (Lowe, 1979).

Another model is the Family Enrichment Program developed by the Lutheran Church in America (Family Enrichment Groups, 1976). This program is for families that are functioning without problems but want a chance to share resources.

Implementation

What is needed, then, is a decision whether to actually apply the support system concept within the parish. If the answer is "yes," there needs to be a commitment of funds and resources, and there must be sanction by the church leadership. There should be some survey research, needs assessment, identification of the most appropriate models, and development of a program on a small scale with the possibility that other Synods or Districts could use the program. Funds will be needed to train people and to conduct training sessions for congregations and ministers who are interested in utilizing support systems for families. There needs to be evaluation and modification of supportive models as they are implemented. And there needs to be a way to maintain the program by institutionalizing it within an office of the church's organizational structure at the Synod or National level.

This paper has attempted to provide a conceptual framework for examining the church as a support to families. It has described healthy family functioning, the stresses most commonly faced by families, and the methods they use to cope with that stress. Research on the supportive functions of the parish is sparse but the findings of support helpful to families in a variety of other settings provide a direction for the church and for this conference in its attempt at model building and implementation of approaches to health and healing in the parish.

BIBLIOGRAPHY

Barnhill, L. "Healthy Family Systems," *Family Coordinator*, Jan. 1979, pp. 94-100.
Beam, W. "College Students' Perceptions of Family Strengths." In N. Stinnett, B. Chesser and

J. DeFrain (Eds.) *Building Family Strengths.* Lincoln, Nebraska: University of Nebraska Press, 1979, pp. 31-37.

Caplan, G. "Organization of Support Systems for Civilian Populations." In G. Caplan and M. Killilea (Eds.) *Support Systems and Mutual Help.* New York: Grune & Stratton, 1976, pp. 273-315.

Caplan, G. & Killilea, M. *Support Systems and Mutual Help.* New York: Grune & Stratton, 1976.

Caplan, Ruth B. *Helping The Helpers to Help: The Development and Evaluation of Mental Health Consultation to Aid Clergymen in Pastoral Work* (New York: Seabury Press, 1972).

Colletta, Nancy. "Support Systems After Divorce: Incidence and Impact." *Journal of Marriage and the Family,* Nov. 1979, pp. 837-846.

Daehling, E. *Developing Support Systems:* A Manual for Lutheran Church Women, Synodical Units, 1977.

Dean, A. and Lin, N. "The Stress Buffering Role of Social Support: Problems & Prospects for Systematic Investigation." *Journal of Nervous and Mental Disease,* 1977, 165: pp. 403-417.

"Family Enrichment Groups," 1976, Division for Parish Services. LCA, 2900 Queen Lane, Philadelphia, Pa. 19129.

Hansen, D. and Johnson, V. "Rethinking Family Stress Theory: Definitional Aspects." In Wesley Burr, et al. *Contemporary Theories About the Family,* Vol. I, New York: The Free Press, 1979.

Haynes, S. and Feinleib, M. "Women, Work and Coronary Heart Disease: Perspective Findings from the Framingham Study." *American Journal of Public Health,* 1980, 70, 2, pp. 133-141.

Hill, R. and Hansen, D. "The Family in Disaster." In G. Baker and D. Chapman (Eds.) *Man and Society in Disaster.* New York: Basic Books, 1962 pp. 185-220.

Lee, Gary. "Effects of Social Networks on the Family." In Burr et al. *Contemporary Theories About the Family.* Vol. I. Free Press, 1979, pp. 27-56.

Lin, N., Ensel, W., Simeone, R. and Juo, W. "Social Support, Stressful Life Events and Illness: A Model and an Empirical Test." *Journal of Health and Social Behavior,* 1979, 20, pp. 108-119.

Lowe, Kathy. "Family Power!" *One World,* World Council of Churches, No. 52, Dec. 1979.

Lynch. *The Broken Heart.* New York: Basic Books, 1977.

McCubbin, H. "Integrating Coping Behavior in Family Stress Theory." *Journal of Marriage and the Family,* May 1979, pp. 237-244.

Moore, K. and Hofferth, S. "Women and Their Children." In Smith, R. *The Subtle Revolution: Women at Work.* Washington, D.C.: The Urban Institute, 1979.

Norquist, LeRoy. "Family Dynamics in the Bible." Unpublished manuscript, Chicago: Lutheran School of Theology, 1979.

Nuckolls, C. G., J. Cassel, & B. H. Kaplan. "Psycho-social Assets, Life Crises and the Prognosis of Pregnancy." *American Journal of Epidemiology,* 1972, 95: pp. 431-441.

Pearlin, L. and Schooler. "The Structure of Coping." *Journal of Health and Social Behavior,* 1978, 19, p. 2-21.

Speck, R. V. & Attneane, C. L. *Family Networks.* New York: Random House, 1973.

Smith, R. *The Subtle Revolution; Women at Work.* Washington, D.C.: The Urban Institute, 1979.

Snapper, K. and Ohms, J. *The Status of Children: 1977,* Washington, D.C.; DHEW Publication No. (OHDS) 78: 30133.

Stinnett, "In Search of Strong Families." In N. Stinnett, B. Chesser and J. DeFrain (Eds.) *Building Family Strengths.* Lincoln, Nebraska: University of Nebraska Press, 1979, pp. 23-30.

Sussman, M. "The Isolated Nuclear Family: Fact or Fiction." *Social Problems,* 6, 1959, pp. 333-339.

Sussman, M. and Burchinal, L. Kin. "Family Network: Unhearalded Structure in Current Conceptualizations of Family Functioning." *Marriage and Family Living,* 24, 1962, pp. 231-240.

Tolsdorf. "Social Networks Support and Coping." *Family Process.* Dec. 1976, 15, pp. 407-417.

Uzoka, A. "The Myth of the Nuclear Family." *The American Psychologist,* 1979, 34, 11, 1097.

Weiss, Robert. "Transition States and Other Stressful Situations: Their Nature and Programs for their Management." In Caplan, G. and Killilea, M. *Support Systems and Mutual Help.* New York: Grune and Stratton, 1976, pp. 213-

Dr. Granger Westberg

CHAPTER VII

From Hospital Chaplaincy to Wholistic Health Center

by Granger E. Westberg

After spending eighteen years as a minister in teaching and research hospitals, I began to wonder if I wanted to spend the rest of my professional life in these settings. I was developing a growing dissatisfaction with my ability to make any significant contributions to the healing of patients who were so critically ill.

The question I kept asking myself was, "Where can a minister's talents best be used in the health field?" I had no regrets for the years I spent doing the best job I could attempting to relate to physicians, nurses, and other staff, but I just wasn't satisfied doing this the rest of my life.

Perhaps the greatest satisfaction I had at the University of Chicago was our weekly Religion-Medicine Case Conference which was a brown-bag affair on Thursday noons at which time a patient's problem was presented by a student chaplain, a resident physician, a nurse, and often a social worker. Whenever possible, we invited the patient's own pastor to participate in the discussion.

In these Religion-Medicine Case Conferences, I began to sense that, for the first time, ministers were at least beginning to converse as equals with physicians concerning patients, and often we had something to offer which had not occurred to the physicians present. In the group—numbering anywhere from a dozen to three dozen professionals—there would often ensue a productive dialogue concerning what clergy can do in assisting patients back to health. However, often we found ourselves talking more about sociology and medicine than about spiritual needs of the patient, and frequently someone in the group would challenge us as to why we called it a *Religion*-Medicine Case Conference. It was much easier to discuss the medical side of a case than the spiritual. Even when we brought in top-flight theologians from the theological faculty of the University, they had difficulty applying religious dimensions to a patient's clinical situation. But we worked at it week after week, and sometimes it became quite an effective means of communication. We chaplains felt good about this new interchange taking place between doctors and ministers. Prior to that, we had seen the doctor only in the role of the captain of the team

Reprinted from *The Journal of Pastoral Care*, June 1979, Vol. XXXIII, No. 2

or as a lecturer to our group where we dutifully took notes. But the doctor was clearly in charge, and we were not sure where we stood as members of the health team—or if we were really on it!

After a number of years at the University of Chicago, I began to ask myself the question, "Is there some other area where my talents as a pastor would be more valuable in the health care system of our day?" The question was forced upon me by conversations with patients prior to radical surgery or medical treatment.

I think of a man in his late 40s who came in to have half his stomach removed because of an ulcerous condition. I asked him when it all started with him. When did his stomach begin to give him trouble? He said, "I can practically pinpoint it to ten years ago when our son was then sixteen years old. He got in trouble with the law—serious trouble—and was put in jail. This was the first time that anybody, any member of our family, had ever been in jail. It was so upsetting to my wife and me that both of us got sick. I developed severe abdominal pains and went to a doctor who gave me some medications which helped me until the time of the trial. Then the pains got worse, and I had to go back for increased dosages. Following the trial and our son's jail sentence, I developed ulcers, and I've been living with these ulcers for some ten years. Finally, my doctor said I would just have to have radical surgery."

This man's gradual movement toward serious illness caused me to do some thinking along the following lines: What if, instead of being his chaplain here in the hospital, I had been a chaplain in the doctor's office ten years before? Suppose the doctor and I had an arrangement whereby we saw all new patients together. We would have heard this man's story, the doctor would have given his prescription, and I would then have invited this man into my office for further conversation. I would have encouraged him to express some of these very deep feelings that were tearing him apart inside. Then, because this was an emergency, I would have invited him to return the next day with his wife, and the three of us would have talked and talked and probably cried a bit and talked some more. And then, as any minister would do, I would go down to the jail and visit his son to try to understand what went wrong. What can I do to help to bring about some kind of communication between these two generations?

And then the doctor and I, over the next several months or maybe the next couple years, would do the best job we could to deal with the entire family and not treat just a stomach. And perhaps that man would not have had to come into our hospital ten years later to have half his stomach removed. This kind of experience, with hundreds of patients, forced me to decide that someday I would like to get into one of the earlier acts of illness where my expertise as a pastor could possibly help to reverse the process and keep people from having to get sicker.

Some years later, in 1967, I found myself teaching practical theology at Hamma School of Theology at Wittenberg University in Springfield, Ohio. I had previously written an article on the subject of having theological students spend up to fifty percent of their time outside the seminary walls where they might find out what was going on in the world and learn how to deal with the current questions instead of the ones that were being asked in 1521. Now this seminary was calling my bluff and asked me to test out some of these ideas.

In addition to my teaching chores within the seminary walls, I spent a good part of my time in a neighborhood church as an associate pastor. This was a very low-income neighborhood with 80% Appalachian whites, 20% blacks, and 15% unemployed. I struggled to relate the seminary students to the neighborhood types of problems and to see if the Gospel had anything to say in such a setting. Soon we found ourselves in close relationship to the local Emerson Elementary School where the school nurse, a black woman, challenged us to take seriously that this was the sickest neighborhood in all of Springfield. She said that there were no physicians in the entire community; that when people were ill they had to go to the hospital emergency room; and that the ambulance made more calls in this neighborhood than in any other neighborhood in all of Springfield. So we put our heads together and came up with the idea that if we could have a doctor's office in our church, we would surround the doctor with seminary students who would be glad to talk to patients at length to get to know them as people, to make house calls, and to try our best to see that their health care would be more than just care of the physical body. Soon we were able to open this first Wholistic Health Center called "Neighborhood Church Clinic" and got volunteer doctors, volunteer nurses, and a number of volunteer lay people to assist us.

We opened the Center in 1969 and after a short period of hesitation, the people in the neighborhood began to trust us and came in large numbers. It was a free clinic, and the volunteer ladies at the front desk would try to explain to patients coming in that in this Center they would be seen not only by a doctor and nurse, but also by a young minister. Ninety-five percent of the patients accepted this without any complaint, but the other five percent, mostly men, resisted the idea that they would have to talk to a minister. The volunteers would explain that the minister would not preach at them; he would merely take a social history and try to get acquainted. If the man continued to resist, the volunteer would add a little humor to her cajoling, and even though this was a free clinic, she would say, "There's no extra charge to see a minister."

This wasn't very convincing either, but the young minister would be called, and soon he and this man would be off in one of the Sunday School rooms getting acquainted. Some of these men told us later that they had enjoyed their conversation with the minister, and some of them said it was the first time in their lives anyone had ever bothered to take them seriously and had listened to them.

The seminary student would then accompany the patient to the doctor and in a capsulated form, in the presence of the patient, tell the doctor what they had talked about. Some of the doctors appreciated this; others did not and wanted to get on with their care of the body without going into any of the details concerning the human factors.

111

However, within about a year, the women at the front desk were reporting to the staff that some of these men who were returning for a second illness and who had resisted the idea of a conversation with a minister the first time, were now leaning over the desk and saying in a quiet voice, "I'm not sure that I need to see a doctor, but I would like to talk to one of the ministers." At this point, the ladies couldn't resist saying, "Oh, there's no extra charge to see a doctor."

From my point of view, this was an indication that people in general, even in a very unsophisticated neighborhood such as this one, are aware that illness is more than just a physical problem and always includes a human or spiritual dimension. I found that our young ministers were thrilled with their experiences because they felt that they had something to offer these people. Because the patients were usually in the early stages of illness, the possibility for reversal of symptoms was greatly increased.

Before, when I was teaching seminary students clinical pastoral care in a hospital setting, I found they often were so in awe of physicians that they depreciated their own value and expressed the wish that they could be doctors who "really do things for patients. All we ministers do is talk to them."

Now, in the Wholistic Health Center setting, they had quite the opposite point of view. They observed how often the care which a doctor gives sick people is only temporary, symptomatic treatment which really doesn't get at the heart of the problem. They now experienced themselves as ministers dealing with the more basic problems and assisting people to rethink ways of living that could bring about health to the body. In the Wholistic Health Center setting I heard theological students actually say, "I'm glad I'm a minister and not a doctor because we're dealing with the most important aspects of illness, and doctors are just dealing with symptoms."

All my professional life I have been trying to get pastors to think more highly of themselves than they do. Because of their low self-esteem, they tend not to do as good a job as they are capable of doing. But when they are able to see patients in a Wholistic Health Center in a church setting, new kinds of self-confidence develop.

I began to understand that teaching seminary students pastoral care in a large teaching and research hospital was one of the most difficult assignments we could ever give a young man or woman. To walk into a room of a patient who had not asked for him, who had no idea what this chaplain was going to do to him, and who may have had bad experiences with clergy in the past, and to expect this young minister to be able, in a brief period of time, to develop such rapport that the patient would confide in him, was to expect more than could happen very often. In fact, I saw many students in the hospital setting become discouraged because most of their conversations were of a chit-chat nature, and they had hoped for something deeper to happen.

By contrast, the students at the Wholistic Health Center were able to engage patients immediately in a discussion of their illness and details concerning life experiences which were affecting their bodies. The students were in a position then to take the problem from its beginning, to work through the physical part with the aid of a doctor and then continue a relationship with the patient as they dealt with the life situations—even making home calls and becoming acquainted with the entire family in such a way that real change could be observed. The young minister began to develop self-confidence much more quickly because he felt that what he was dealing with was somewhat manageable and within his own area of competence. Soon the seminary students were developing seminars and discussion groups for patients, getting volunteers to help design courses in nutrition, cooking, sewing, child care, stress management, etc.

After the Center had been in operation a little over a year, I was invited to Howard Medical School in Washington, D.C., where the students showed great interest in the idea of a doctor's office in a church with the addition of counseling and health education programs. They liked the idea that all of this could be done within the context of a parish church where space was available and could serve a dual purpose for both a clinic and for Sunday School purposes.

But soon these Howard Medical students were raising the question, "Are you planning to do this only in low-income neighborhoods?" And I replied that I was, in fact, planning a second clinic in an all-black area of the city. Their response surprised me. They said, "If you do this only in low-income neighborhoods, you're going to give the impression that this is just poor people's medicine and that if these poor people ever got any money, they wouldn't want that kind of medicine. They'd want what the rich people have—pure scientific medicine without any of this counseling and health education business." They said, "Why don't you try this in middle-income churches where the people of the community could pay their own way and the doctor and the nurse and the minister could be on salary and carry on an effective program that would be self-supporting?"

Then one of the students said, "Why don't you even try it in rich neighborhoods? Rich pepole need this kind of care more than anybody. They're all mixed up."

Coming back from Washington, D.C., I began to dream of the possibility of testing out this model in a church in an affluent neighborhood, knowing that if we started with the upper-income neighborhood, it would always be easier to move to the middle and then the lower-income communities than it would be to go in the other direction.

I then took my sabbatical year early and spent that year visiting medical schools and hospitals attempting to see whether this concept made any sense to medical educators. I ended up at the University of Illinois Medical School in Chicago where the head of the Department of Preventive Medicine invited me to join the faculty and develop model Wholistic Health Centers in relation to the department of Family Practice. And so we opened our first Center, with the help of the W. K. Kellogg Foundation's support, in a suburb of Chicago called Hinsdale in Union Church—United Church of Christ. We used residents from family practice programs and volunteer nurses from the community along with our own staff of pastoral counselors.

The first year was very slow going because the people of Hinsdale couldn't understand why we would need a "clinic" in a church in such a neighborhood. Church clinics normally serve poor people and there were no poor people in Hinsdale. One doctor said, "Granger, why in the world are you starting a Center in Hinsdale? We have more doctors per square foot in Hinsdale than in almost any other western suburb of Chicago. The last thing we need is another doctor's office here."

The only answer I could think to give him was: "We must test out this model in the midst of the finest medical care obtainable in a community where the people can well afford to pay any price for health care. If these people are willing to come into a doctor's office in a church, of all places, I am sure we can get other Centers going any place in the country."

Our earliest patients were nurses who came from all over the county saying that they had been searching for doctors who would give wholistic care and had been unable to find any. The next group were social workers, and the third group were school teachers. By that time, we had enough patients to begin to become self-supporting. Now, in 1979, people from all income levels are numbered among our patients.

We soon discovered that it wasn't only the nurses who were angry about our present American health care system, but that people in general were very dissatisfied with the impersonal care they were receiving. They particularly liked the fact that we set aside half an hour for all new patients on their first visit for a discussion in a relaxed atmosphere with the doctor, the minister, and the nurse. The minister became the moderator of this first discussion because the doctor and the nurse would have their opportunity to ask more specifically medical questions the next half hour when the patient went into the examining room for a complete physical.

During this first period, which we call a Health Planning Conference, it becomes clear to the patient that the clergyperson is a very active member of this healing team and that he or she has a way of inviting patients to discuss life situations that may have had some effect on their health. The doctors were frequently surprised by the way patients would relate some of the deepest things that were going on within them and not hesitate to express anxieties, doubts, fears, as well as hopes, ambitions, and religious values. The following week the patient would return, and we would have his lab test back and any Xray findings. We would then sit down again—more briefly this time—to discuss treatment plans. We were more than pleased with the number of patients who, when asked what they would like to do about their present health situation, would say that, in addition to seeing the doctor and the nurse, they would like to have discussions with the pastoral counselor.

As I look back on what has happened through these health planning conferences, I realize that the minister has now been brought into the diagnostic process and that this is what I felt was missing from my ministry in a hospital setting.

I realized that I was vaguely aware that many of the patients with whom I

114

worked in the hospital had not been properly worked up and that, because I had not participated in the discussion with these patients in the presence of the doctor, the human problems and the spiritual problems had been completely ignored. I realized that the sort of training which physicians receive in medical school develops a kind of tunnel vision which makes it impossible for them to believe that there are spiritual dimensions to illness which need to be taken just as seriously as the physical.

And this is where I stand today in my concern for wholistic health care. I am convinced that if a patient's diagnosis is made only by a physician, the patient cannot possibly be treated wholistically. Certainly the converse of this would also be true if the patient were diagnosed only by a minister. Here, with a team of doctor, minister *and* a nurse, who acts as the patient's advocate and a kind of catalyst between medicine and religion, new kinds of things happen in such a discussion that could not ever happen if the patient were only seeing one of these persons.

I am fully aware that what we call wholistic health care is not really whole person care to the extent that it ought to be. Some, in humor, have suggested that we call these "Halfistic" Centers because we are really only dealing, even yet, with a small part of the patient's life needs.

We now have six Centers in the Chicagoland area and others in Minneapolis, Cleveland, Washington, D.C. We are learning how to bring patients into the diagnostic process as well as the healing process in ways that help patients learn how to take care of themselves and relinquish the need for professionals to make decisions for them. We find that our "compliance" rate (a very bad word) is much higher than is found in the traditional doctor's office where the doctor makes all the decisions because the doctor "knows best." We operate on the basis that the patient probably knows better than anybody in the room, and we are only his resource people. Ultimately, patients have to decide what changes they want to make in their life styles that will increase their chances of healthy living. We are encouraged by the number of patients who are taking their health care into their own hands.

Rev. Joel Hempel

Ms. Jill Westberg

CHAPTER VIII

Six Action Models of Ministry

1. CONGREGATIONS ORGANIZING FOR MISSION ENDEAVOR

C.O.M.E. is the unique and proven model for congregational and individual renewal through churchly small groups that are part of the total congregational structure.

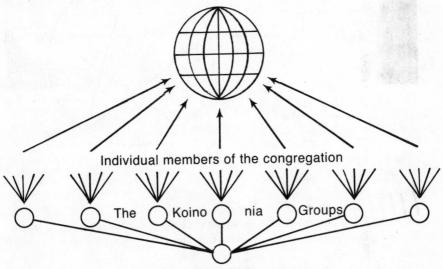

Individual members of the congregation

The Koinonia Groups

The Koinonia Leaders Group

C.O.M.E. provides all the help and resources that are needed to launch and maintain this effective program which is already working in more than 100 congregations:
- Carefully planned and personalized seminars for pastors and other leaders to acquaint people with the model and the study program. "The seminar gave me the confidence and know-how that I needed." Presbyterian pastor, Minneapolis.
- The study program consisting of 31 lessons that in effect constitute a mini-seminary curriculum for training people to carry on effective, theologically-informed pastoral care ministries for each other.
- On-going counsel and guidance as you need it and request it.
- Newsletters, advanced seminars, and other aids to growth.

C.O.M.E. defines discipleship as the life-long process in which Christians help each other to reach ever greater commitment in living out their baptismal vocation to imitate Christ for the sake of their neighbor in the daily situations of life.

C.O.M.E. builds its total program around the five basic functions of worship, fellowship, nurture, witness, and service and stresses balanced growth in all five areas as the crucial pattern for lasting discipleship.

WORSHIP: Our joyous and total response in public, family, and private to God's goodness.

FELLOWSHIP: Our cheerful sharing of our strengths, gifts, and possessions.

NURTURE: Mutual growth through study toward Christ's stature.

WITNESS: Being Christlike persons in word and deed.

SERVICE: Individual and organized pursuit of charity and justice.

C.O.M.E. is committed to reasonable charges for its services to enable maximum participation. No congregation will be excluded for financial reasons.

The four-day seminar fee is $300.00 for the first registrant from a congregation, $200.00 each for the next two, fourth and fifth are free. The three-day week-end seminar is $175.00 for the first registrant from a congregation, $125.00 each for the next two, fourth and fifth are free. The afternoon introductory seminar is $50.00 per congregation with no limit on the number that may attend. The Leader's Manual is $19.50 and the Member's Manual is $12.50. The study program is published and distributed by Morse Press, Medford, OR 97501.

Write or call for information and proposed seminars to C.O.M.E., 830 Phyllis Lane, St. Louis, MO 63141, (314) 872-9234. Herbert T. Mayer is Executive Director.

Dr. Kieth Gerberding
Peace Lutheran Church
Southgate, Michigan

2. THE STEPHEN SERIES

ADMINISTRATION:

The Stephen Series is administered by Pastoral Care Team Ministries, a not-for-profit religious and educational organization, interdenominational and international in scope.

LOCATION:

Pastoral Care Team Ministries
7120 Lindell Boulevard
St. Louis, Missouri 63130
(314) 725-0991

PURPOSE:

The purpose of the Stephen Series is to train and organize lay persons to do caring ministry in and around their congregations.

GOALS:

The goals of the Stephen Series are:
1. To make the ministry of a laity a real possibility.
2. To provide solid, practical, understandable, and immediately usable training which will give lay persons the training they need to do meaningful ministry.
3. To give pastors and church leaders the tools they need to truly be "equippers of the saints."
4. To provide a system of organization and administration which enables congregations to set up lay ministry that will *work* and will *last*.
5. To teach people in congregations how to care more effectively so that Christian churches may become warmer, more concerned, more caring places.

PROCEDURES:

The Stephen Series provides congregations with five things:
1. A *Leader's Manual* which provides pastors and congregations with everything they need to train persons in effective caring skills.
2. Trainee manuals which are "hands-on" materials for people being trained in congregations.
3. A system of organization and administration which enables congregations to set up a lay ministry program that will work and will last.
4. A Leader's Training Course which trains you to use the *Leader's Manual* and the Organizational/Administrative system. (Congregations enrolling in the Stephen Series are entitled to unlimited participation in the Stephen Series Leader's Training Courses after paying the one-time enrollment fee.)
5. A continuing relationship of free consultation drawing upon the years of experience of the Stephen Series staff.

119

COSTS:

To enroll in the Stephen Series congregations pay a *one-time* enrollment of $975.00.

After this enrollment fee is paid, the only other costs are for room and board at the Leader's Training Course and for additional materials congregations may want to buy.

FURTHER INFORMATION:

If you would like further information about the Stephen Series, please write or call Dr. Kenneth Haugk, PCTM's Executive Director, at the Stephen Series offices.

At St. Martin's Lutheran Church we are continuing to experience a widened, more effective Christian ministry because of the Stephen Ministers. They are being assigned to people in crisis by the pastors; they are reaching out to people in their places of work and neighborhood; and they are being called upon by members of the congregation for help. Their effectiveness in Christian caring is known. It is exciting to watch this ministry grow, flourish, and expand the work in God's Kingdom.

Dr. Robert D. Hurlbut
St. Martin's Lutheran Church
Austin, Texas

3. BASIC ELEMENTS OF CHRISTIAN CARE

In the paragraphs which follow, thirteen basic elements of Christian care are summarized which are taught in our Inner City Clinical Pastoral Education ministry, located at Prince of Peace Lutheran Church, Cincinnati, Ohio.

These elements which are listed below can be used both within the Christian community and for outreach into the neighborhood. They can be used in individual care or in a group setting as in worship. Although space does not permit to talk about how these elements can be applied to worship, the reader, if one chooses, can think creatively of how to structure the worship setting and service to incorporate these elements of Christian care.

Thirteen elements:

1. Presence—Such presence includes one's body, thinking, feelings, senses, and spirituality. Helping persons work to be as fully present as possible with another.
2. Time—The quantity of time is usually not as important as the quality of time. It is difficult to be caring when Christian helpers are preoccupied with their own schedule or agenda.
3. Listening—
   a) *With* all senses and intuition and the Holy Spirit working in us.
   b) *To* individuals (group), context, and one's self.

c) *For* words, body language, affect, avoidances, wants, needs, values, problems, and resistance.

4. Getting to Know the Person—As the above three elements increase, one increasingly knows the person. As helping people increasingly get to know the ones with whom they are working we want to be curious about their relationship with God, their relationship with other people, and their relationship with themselves.

5. Being Open in Sharing One's Self—The caring relationship remains one-sided unless we are willing to reveal our own being appropriately. Such self revelation includes our likes, our dislikes, fears, struggles, strengths, weaknesses, etc. By sharing our own hurts and needs and weaknesses, we are indicating our willingness to receive ministry as well.

6. Motivation for Caring—comes from one's personal relationship with Jesus Christ. This relationship always has room to mature. Without such a relationship with God, all other ministry that we are about is superficial.

7. Touching—There is a great lack of touching in our society. Yet, it is a very natural need and expression of warmth and affection. Touching, in a very concrete sense, is grace incarnate. To embrace or hold someone who feels hurt or worthless or sad or scared is to communicate our and God's love and strength.

8. Confrontation—When people are thinking or acting or talking destructively, they need to be confronted carefully. Such confrontation does not come out of our hidden hostility. Rather, it is "speaking the truth in the spirit of love." (Ephesians 4:15)

9. Support—Standing with people in what they are feeling and empathizing with them communicates assurance of their value. In effect we are saying, you are worth being with.

10. Communicating God's and the Church's Care—Most important to communicate is our Lord's love and forgiveness within Christian fellowship. Part of Christian fellowship is responding to each other's need. Thus, the promise, "Seek first the kingdom of God and all these things shall be added unto you," implies that it is the church's responsibility to see to it that "all these things" are added. The church is not the church when it turns its back on pain.

11. Use of Religious Resources—God has given to his people many resources which can be used in Christian care. These resources include prayer, the Lord's Supper, confession and absolution, baptism, the local congregation as an extended family, the gifts of the Spirit, one's personal relationship with Christ, etc. To consistently disregard these resources in ministry is to disregard great power that is available to us.

12. The Resources of the Neighborhood—along with one's own personal resources as well as the resources of the individuals with whom one is working. It is important for us to know ourselves, our strengths and limitations, and the extent to which we are able to give of ourselves. Likewise,

the people we care for need to discover the same about themselves. Hopefully, where our individual resources end, the neighborhood resources can give what is needed. Thus it becomes very important to know our neighborhoods and what they have to offer.

13. Clarifying and Sorting Out Facts and Determining What the Options Are— for the people with whom we are working. In caring for people, we want to find out the facts about what their problems are, their needs, their resources, their priorities, etc. We then want to be able to help the person to determine what can be changed in his life and what his alternatives are in making those changes happen. This is especially important when working with someone who feels overwhelmed by his problems.

In reviewing these thirteen elements of Christian care, there are a couple of summary statements I want to make. One is that elements one through six are required in *all* contacts with people to whom we are offering care. However, elements seven through thirteen are "tools" which can be used as needed to intensify the relationship and/or help the person move toward maturity and fulfillment as God's person.

The second summary comment I want to make is that there is nothing inherent in these elements that indicate that they can only be used by clergy. All people who are willing can further develop their caring skills. Lay people as well as pastors need to be trained in giving care so that our congregations may increasingly become caring and health-giving communities.

In the Inner City Clinical Pastoral Education program offered out of Prince of Peace Church in Cincinnati, Ohio, people come from across the country to work at further developing these basic elements in Christian care. Although they work within the inner city context, the skills that are learned can be applied either within the poverty community or in any context where a person seeks to offer care. The students learn by being actively involved in ministry and then returning to the classroom setting to reflect with the supervisor on what they have experienced.

We have found that people become more effective in their caring as they experience integration of their personality with how they think and how they relate to other people. In other words, we want people in the training program to know what they believe and what impact it has on them as people and on those with whom they minister. We also want them to be able to express what they believe in ways that make sense. It is also critical for an effective caring ministry, for helping people to know what within ourselves and our personalities enhances our ministry and what within us gets in the way of ministry. In coming to a better understanding of ourselves we are more able to determine what needs to be changed in ourselves so that we can become more effective ministers; and secondly, so that we can affirm ourselves in our uniqueness. Becoming an integrated person also means developing alternative ways of interacting with people making use of our personalities and our beliefs.

There is much more that could be said about the Inner City Clinical

Pastoral Education program. If you are interested in finding out more of the details, you may contact Joel Hempel at Prince of Peace Lutheran Church, 1522 Race Street, Cincinnati, Ohio 45210.

4. THE HEALTH CABINET

At the Community of Christ the Servant (CCS) in Lombard, Illinois we have a pilot ministry which we are calling the Health Cabinet. The purpose of the Cabinet is to promote all aspects of the healing ministry at CCS. Having this one ministry that concentrates solely on health (to the whole person in the context of community) makes possible a more extensive and effective healing ministry than ever before.

The Health Cabinet is made up of volunteers from our church (some are health professionals, some are not) who are committed to seeing our healing ministry become one which will touch everyone at CCS in their joy and their suffering. The Health Cabinet assists individuals and families to become more responsible for maintaining and improving their own health and that of their community. While the Cabinet will not be involved in the diagnosis and treatment of individuals, it will greatly step up the promotion of healthy behavior and ensure strong support to individuals who are not well. The Health Cabinet will act as a source of influence in the life of the church community to ensure that the stewardship of health is expressed in worship, education, networks of support, and recreation.

The Cabinet sponsors or supports health-related programs. These include events like recreation, support groups, courses on stress or C.P.R. training. Wherever possible it tries to incorporate programs into groups that already meet regularly like educational classes and social groups.

More important than any of the programming that is done is the promotion of an atmosphere which is supportive of health for the whole person. Basically the Cabinet does this by looking at the total life of the church, in all its health and ''unhealth.''

For instance, the Cabinet might examine the worship service. Has worship become a private affair between a worshipper and God or is there also an emphasis on the community relationship? Are people alive to the healing elements of the Eucharist? Is there an opportunity to share concerns and celebrations? Is the worship experienced as being concerned with what is personal and relevant?

There are many aspects of church life which the Health Cabinet discusses and acts upon. For instance, visitors—are they truly made to feel welcome? Are people who have made it through difficult times (divorce, chronic illness, peer pressure) aware of others who are now facing similar difficulties so that they might be of help? Is there an atmosphere which encourages people to struggle with their values and beliefs? Are people supported in the risks that they dare to take? When a member of the congregation becomes very ill, are there steps taken to inform and educate the entire congregation so that they have an understanding of this person's situation?

There are abundant possibilities for a healing ministry which we have only begun to tap at CCS. As an experimental model we are testing out new approaches in hopes of uncovering some of those untapped possibilities. We are gradually learning what works and what doesn't. While our model still has a long way to go, we are hopeful that our work is a significant step in the direction of revitalizing congregations' ministry in the area of health.

Jill Westberg
Christ the Servant Lutheran Church
Lombard, Illinois

5. MODEL: LINKAGE BETWEEN PARISH MINISTRY/INSTITUTIONAL CHAPLAINCY

SITUATION: Trinity Lutheran Church, Memphis, Tennessee is a 100 year old downtown congregation. It is the mother church of 21 Lutheran churches in greater Memphis (twelve LC-MS, four LCA, four ALC, one WIS. Synod). It is located in the shadow of federal, state, city, and county office buildings. The fourteen story courthouse being erected a few yards to the west of the church, and a six story jail being erected immediately to the east of the church, both connected with a two story structure and tunnels on the north side of the church, are only part of the rebuilding and revitalization of downtown Memphis. There are 6000 hospital beds within a mile and a half of Trinity. The University of Tennessee Medical Units are the core of this vast Medical Complex.

THE PROFILE OF TRINITY CONGREGATION. Trinity today is made up of approximately 340 communicants and 400 baptized members who live within a radius of 30 miles of the church. Many of her members are elderly. We have 40 shutins. Trinity's extended congregation includes 76 guest members (newcomers, University students, and other Lutherans still not identified with a local Lutheran church), 93 prospects (people who are not now closely identified with any church and whom we consider our spiritual responsibility), 202 medical contacts (patients throughout the Mid South to whom we have ministered on an extended basis and/or repeatedly during the past two decades and with whom we maintain contact), a score of medical people (graduates of University of Tennessee College of Medicine—doctors, dentists, pharmacists, technicians, and graduates of Southern College of Optometry with whom we maintain contact).

PERSONNEL RESOURCES:

Pastor: Paul R. Martens (at Trinity twenty-three years), president of Lutheran Social Services of Tennessee (which has established two high-rise apartments each with 195 units for moderate income elderly and sponsors Project

M.E.E.T. which serves 2400 meals to the elderly five days a week at forty-two serving sites), chaplain at Luther Towers.

Associate Pastor: Ronald J. Wiese (at Trinity four years), President of Downtown Churches Association, President of the Board of Criminal Justice Ministry (an ecumenical group which trains volunteers to work with prisoners on one to one basis), Chairman, District Board of Social Ministry.

Two Secretaries: One employed, one volunteer.

Sixteen members who have been given Pastoral Care Team Ministry Training (Stephen Series), sixteen Bethel Bible trainees.

Six elders and six stewards.

Four members of Board of Evangelism.

A host of sensitive, caring and praying members.

MINISTRY: Services and Bible classes

Close contact with membership of congregation and constantly reaching out to new prospects.

Dial-A-Devotion—a three minute telephone taped inspirational message available twenty-four hours a day, changed daily.

Noon Day Book Reviews—Spring and fall series (each eight weeks) conducted since 1967—outreach to downtown community (average attendance 70 at last series)

University students—through Interfaith Center.

Hospitals—Average of 20 Lutherans daily in downtown hospitals (6000 beds).

Prison Ministry—Weekly Bible class in downtown prison (40 prison capacity). New prison adjacent to church to be opened in 1981 to house 1224 prisoners.

Supportive of—Downtown Churches of Food Pantry—members to bring canned food first Sunday of each month.

Mustard Seed—PAN-Lutheran store for the poor, dealing primarily in clothing.

LINKAGE OF INSTITUTION CHAPLAINCY AND PARISH MINISTRY

Both pastors have been designated institutional chaplains by the Mid South District of the Lutheran Church—Missouri Synod. In this capacity they—

1. Assign pastor and lay contact for every hospital in Memphis, themselves ministering to the downtown hospitals.
2. Work closely with retired chaplain who serves as juvenile court chaplain.
3. Utilize PCTM volunteers to minister to hospitalized, nursing home patients, and other shutins.
4. Keep hospitalized before membership of the congregation in—"Remember in Prayer" paragraph in Sunday bulletin and also mentioning them and their situations in meetings of Church Council, Elders, and four Circles urging prayerful concern and support.
5. Maintain extensive contact with Mid South pastors with reference to pa-

tients, frequently referring prospects to congregations.

Pastors Martens and Wiese share responsibilities of parish and chaplaincy assuring efficient continuity of ministry.

Paul R. Martens
Trinity Lutheran Church
204 Washington Ave.
Memphis, TN 38103
Phone: 901-525-1056

6. AGING MINISTRY MODELS FOR PARISHES

BACKGROUND—Aging Ministry work in the Florida Synod—LCA began in 1973 when several delegates attended an LCA Symposium on Aging in Pittsburgh, Pennsylvania.

When the group returned, they became convinced that a Task Force on Aging should be organized and a research study on the needs of older Florida Lutherans be begun. After four years of work, a major research project involving hundreds of people and thousands of man-hours was completed.

Computerized findings from the compilation of data taken from the 17-page interview schedule used on 300 Florida Lutherans (LCA, LCMS, and ALC) revealed that over 25% of these Lutherans were lonely most of the time, that over-sixty Lutherans expected their church to become heavily involved in providing ministry to their expected needs. (Full details have been published in a 3-volume booklet entitled ''Golden Opportunities.)

FLORIDA LUTHERAN AGING MINISTRIES—In 1978 FLAM was developed as an attempt to utilize these findings in a programmatic action in a specific parish. In addition, Pastor Hafer is to be available as Consultant for parishes requesting his help in building their own parish ministries.

Some of the Models already developed include:

1. The Half-way and Over Club developed at Emmanuel Lutheran Church, Venice, Florida, a 200-member social club in that church which developed not only many very active social functions, but also developed some drama, a Christmas dinner for forty-five senior persons who would have eaten alone, a Friendly Visitor program, a Home and Nursing Home Visit program, a Tape Ministry, bus trips, a training session by Paramedics, a family Sunday Church School summer enrichment program, prayer breakfasts, etc.

The Model indicates the importance of establishing a very viable social group that then nurtures the growth of many other ministries for the congregation and the community.

2. The Later Life Seminar for professionals in the field of Gerontology and church members who wanted to learn more about aging themes. The second Seminar emphasized Widowed-Support Systems, Stress and Anxiety, Resource Building, and Aging and Sexuality.

126

3. A seminar which helped people to understand various kinds of losses and how ministry could occur to those in loss.

4. A development of a full-service Retirement Center for middle income people.

5. A Senior Staffer program—where retired persons are employed half-time by the Lutheran Bodies to begin working with congregations to develop their Aging Ministry programs. A full training program and support system was necessarily built around the three Senior Staffers chosen.

6. The developing of the booklet, "Now That We Have Time" for use with congregations who want to begin ministry with aging persons.

7. Week-long bus-trips.

8. A consultant network of professionals who provide a support system for Senior Staffers and are available to solve knotty problems in the Gerontological field.

9. The development of a Widowed-to-Widowed support program.

PLANS FOR THE FUTURE:

Some Models that we have in the planning stages are—

1. Adult Day Care
2. A Retired Reliables—Resource and skill bank of retired persons and a referral system for those in need (using the church office as referral agent).
3. Free retirement planning programs.
4. An Aging and Sexuality Consultant.
5. Additional Seminars on "Successful Aging" and other meaningful topics for retirees and those who work with them.

The Rev. Richard J. Hafer
900 Tamiami Trail South
Venice, FL 33595
(813) 488-4422
(813) 488-3456

Dr. David T. Stein

CHAPTER IX

Hospital and Church: Helpmates in Ministry

By David T. Stein

In his study of institutional revolution published in 1970 under the title, "Celebration of Awareness," Ivan D. Illich says: "I believe that the specific task of the church in the modern world is the Christian celebration of the experience of change. The future has already broken into the present. We each live in many times. The present of one is the past of another and the future of yet another." This is a logical contradiction much like that of the author of Hebrews when he writes about Jesus the Christ as "the same yesterday and today and forever" (Hebrews 13:8).

The role of the Lutheran hospital past, present, and future has not been the same yesterday, today nor—would I guess—forever. Yet at the same time the hospital struggles to be the same. Even with changes from the little black bag to the world of the ultra modern clinical hospital, from home-caring MD's to sub-sub-subspecialists in hospital office spaces, the art of healing has really not changed.

The role of the Lutheran hospital in the past was one of receiver. It collected bodies and processed them for better living through chemistry, surgery, and psychotherapy. It was concerned with the clinical, medical care of patients. Its relations to parishes were passive.

The hospital was a model for overseas medical missions. It may have given attention to hunger, disease, ignorance, and poverty, but its larger focus was the evangelization of the world. Essentially it planted western modules. Medical care before alien environments paid little attention to the cultural needs of the people. It was a glamorous story of Camelot, where doctors were saints and nurses just helpers and where few pastoral missionaries cared to go.

The Lutheran hospital has had difficulty moving away from the image of a place "where doctors and nurses and all kinds of medical and submedical specialists are trained for handling acute illnesses," according to a prominent hospital administrator. He says the hospital is still a "doctor's workshop where the nurses are like a pool of secretaries and all other personnel are part of the custodial staff."

129

Fundamentally, the Lutheran hospital and the community hospital were and are no different. Third-party reimbursings and federal and state programs keep the Lutheran hospital from a unique place among community hospitals. It has been and continues to be a "not-for-prophet" part of the health care industry.

I am part of an unusually staffed hospital, Lutheran General of Park Ridge, Ill., where 3,640 employees work every 24 hours. The staff includes 55 pastorally trained, ordained, and credentialed persons doing ministry in one institution.

Now in its 20th year, Lutheran General is moving out of a patriarchal period of human ecology into an organizational and administrative period of wholism, facilitated by a poly-corporate structure of health care and allied services. The new element of this outlook is that we are learning how to manage more than we can understand. The health care industry has grown so rapidly and the technology has become so complex that the big struggle is how we can humanize ourselves in order not to treat the patient as nothing more than a scientific experiment.

Furthermore, how do we keep the chaplains' pastoral care pastoral when some have adopted clinical medical jargon? Isolation in the clinical unit is a danger. Even the conversation among the nonclinically trained is strained when the hospital chaplain uses a medical shorthand full of acronyms and types of medical and diagnostic care.

At present the Lutheran hospital is struggling with itself. But as it struggles, it is doing some new things and a lot of old things for and with the parish. The relationship is active. The concern is for wholistic patient care.

Lutheran General has programs for the aged and for families, nursing education efforts, outpatient psychotherapy satellites based in parishes and CME (clinical ministry education) programs for lay people. Other activities include transgenerational studies, hospice development, grief groups, cancer care groups, and crisis care intervention.

With most of these and other opportunities provided by Lutheran General its division of pastoral care has taken the initiative in addressing the needs of parishes, their clergy and lay members. Interestingly, the medical side has to be coaxed out of the hospital, while social workers, pastors and educators of all varieties are beating a path to the parish, often in competition rather than in cooperation.

I like what is happening at Lutheran General. Even though we find ourselves in the midst of a monolithic structure which is hierarchical in style, ours is not a quiet, paper-shuffling organization with orders handed down from above. Instead it is a dynamic, healthy mix of professionals, each trying to do the best thing to prevent illness rather than cure it and in that commitment raising all sorts of questions and dilemmas for the medical world.

What about the future? We face radical, life-and-death issues. "So what's new?" you say. "The hospital has been here all along from birth to death." But the future is not so simple. We are just beginning to learn about the structuring and restructuring of genes, the dilemmas of euthanasia and new types of families.

History gives us a vivid picture of radicals who attempted change. Martin Luther King went to the mountain, Henry David Thoreau to Walden, Mahatma Gandhi to the sea, Christ to Gethsemane. Medicine must make a radical commitment to humane care.

Maybe the transition to that commitment can best be illustrated by an excerpt from the autobiographical statement, "The Night Is Dark and I Am Far From Home," by Jonathan Kozol, one of my favorite authors. He tells of trying to help an epileptic child:

"Tall and thin, 14 years old, she is intense and sober, devastated but unhating. Her life is a staccato sequence of grand mal convulsions. No money, no systems, no advice on how to get a refill of expensive script, of more Dilantin, more phenobarbital.

"This night she comes downstairs to the church office where I work. Within the cloakroom underneath the stairs, standing there and asking me, please, if I would close the door and hold her head within my arms because she knows she's going to have an epileptic seizure. And closing the door and sitting down upon the cold cement while she lies down and places her head within my arms and starts to shudder violently. And moves about so that I scarcely can protect her wracked and thin young body from the cement wall and from the concrete floor. And seeing her mouth writhe up with pain and spittle. And feeling her thrash about the second time and now a third. And in between, the terror closing in upon her as in a child's dream that you can't get out. And watching her then and wondering what she undergoes. And later seeing her exhausted, sleeping there, right in my arms as at the end of a long ordeal, all passion in her spent.

"Then taking her out into my car and driving her to the city hospital where she, as epileptics very often do, keeps saying that she's going to have another seizure. And slamming on the brakes and walking with her in the back door where they receive outpatient cases.

"And being confronted on this winter night at 9 P.M. in Boston in the year of our Lord 1965 with a scene that comes from Dante's Purgatory. Dozens and dozens of poor white, black and Puerto Rican people, infants and mothers, old men, alcoholics, men with hands wrapped in gauze, aged people trembling with fever. One hostile woman in white uniform behind a table telling us, out of a face made, as it seems, of clay, that we should fill an application out— some sort of form, a white sheet, then sit out in the hallway since the waiting room is full. And then to try to say this child had just had several seizures in a row and needs treatment and do we need to do the forms. And, yes of course you need to do the forms right and wait your turn and do not think you have any special right to come ahead of someone else who's been sitting there before you.

"Two hours and four seizures later you go up and go in and shout in her cold eyes and walk right up and grab the intern by the arm and tell him to come

131

out and be a doctor to an epileptic child sitting on a damp rag in the hallway. He comes out and in two minutes he gives this child an injection that arrests the seizure and sedates her, then writes the script for more Dilantin, more phenobarbital. And shakes his head and says to you, it's a damn shame. Nobody needs to have an epileptic seizure in this day and age. Nobody but a poor black nigger, says the intern in a sudden instant of that rage that truth and decency create. He nearly cries. And in his eyes you see a kind of burning pain that tells you that he's a good man somehow. Deep down, some place where it isn't all cold stone and clean surgery and antiseptic reason. Nobody, but a poor black nigger, needs to have an epileptic seizure any more.

"So you take her home. And you go back to the church, down to your office underneath the stairs. And look at the floor. And listen to the silence. And you are 28 years old. And you begin to cry. You cry for more than what that young girl has just been through. And you long not to believe that this can be the city that you really live in. You find it very hard to lock up that idea because it threatens all the things that you have wanted to believe for so long. So you sit alone awhile. And you try to lock those bitter passions in the secret spaces of your self-control. You try to decontaminate your anger and to organize your rage. But you can't do it this time. You just can't build that barrier of logical control a second time."

I do not know the future role of the Lutheran hospital as it relates to the parish. But I know what it should be: a commitment to the best humane, clinical, medical, pastoral and wholistic patient care, integrating the exciting activities of all the helping professions. It should also be a commitment to a suffering servant role of ministry, helping to restore individuals who are broken and to recapture the assurance of and the hope in the great physician, Jesus the Christ, who cleanses all of us from our iniquities and who heals all our diseases.

The parish has a lot to learn from the first-class world of medicine. But that is another topic. As the church has taken on some of the political and bureaucratic savvy of the medical group, maybe—just maybe—the Lutheran hospital will discover in the church a partner, a helpmate in ministry.

Dr. Orval Westby

CHAPTER X

Of Agencies and Congregations

by Orval Westby, Executive Director
Lutheran Social Service System

Wheat Ridge Foundation is to be commended for sponsoring this symposium on "Health and Healing: Ministry of the Church." It is certainly a continuation of the great tradition that Wheat Ridge has established in its first seventy-five years. The goal of this anniversary symposium—"to have North American Lutherans more actively engaged in Christ's healing ministry as individuals and together with others"—is a challenging expression of its vigorous commitment to health and healing ministry.

As a representative of the American Lutheran Church, the Lutheran Church in America, and the Lutheran Church—Missouri Synod who jointly created and support LS/3, I am pleased to be a participant in this symposium. LS/3 is a national office through which these three church bodies cooperate with nearly 300 Lutheran agencies, homes, and institutions in the development and maintenance of social ministries to families and children, the elderly, the handicapped, and disabled, the minorities, the refugees, and the poor. They have been providing these helping and healing ministries for many years, some of them since the early days of Lutheranism in America.

During the nearly 100 years they span, significant changes in the structure and programs of Lutheran social ministry have occurred. In the days of the immigrant church, the parish was the locus of a helping and healing ministry in which the members provided supportive and caring service to each other and their neighbors. Most, if not all, of us know from our ethnic backgrounds about the infra-structure of social ministry in those early days. But as the first and second generations of the native-born moved into a more urbanized and industrialized society, they continued their mutual-aid but also developed societies, homes, and hospitals for the abandoned, the neglected, and the sick. This "inner mission" thrust was eventually superseded by the formation of "agencies and institutions" after World War I. As president of the board of Lutheran Welfare Society of South Dakota in the early 1950's, I read the impressive story of Bertha Bragstad and First Lutheran Church which supported her in the establishment of a home for unmarried mothers in 1921. As with many other social ministries in our church, this was the beginning of what has become a

135

statewide agency—Lutheran Social Services of South Dakota—supported by and serving in partnership with most of the Lutheran congregations in the state. Little did I know in 1951 that almost twenty-five years later as Secretary of the South Dakota Department of Social Services I would then see *from a different perspective* the significant Christian ministry that these congregations were providing. I have woven this personal experience into this sketch of historical changes to emphasize that while the structures and programs of our social ministry have changed, the purpose and motivation remains—to serve others in the name of Christ, and to emphasize the continuing partnership of congregation and agency.

All of us were invited to this symposium to focus on the resources of the congregation for ministries of health and healing. Are there not some new models for ministry that congregations can create out of their own resources? In particular, can the congregation itself become a community of "healers" and of "healing"?

This is a challenging and timely emphasis. All of the psychological and sociological literature of the last twenty years on alienation, fragmentation, etc., underscore the need for ministry to the whole person. As participants in our own congregation and community we are aware of the need for a holistic ministry that we have not yet achieved.

So here we are to discover together how this might come about in our own congregation and in all other congregations.

If we review the major papers and the parish models that we have been presented, some basic observations emerge. For example, can we say that:

1. The congregation commits itself to the ministry of health and healing as integral to its life and mission as the People of God.
2. The diversity of persons and the gifts of each is the most important resource of the congregation for a health and healing ministry.
3. The congregation is open to the innovation of new roles and relationships, to adopting non-traditional modes of ministry, and willing to revise its "life-style" to create a community of "healers" and of "health and healing."

These kinds of extrapolations from the congregation's success or failure with pilot projects can help us create more effective models of health and healing ministry.

Are there roles that agencies, homes, and institutions can perform in their relationships to the congregation? Are there any models of partnership from which we can extrapolate any helpful observations?

Since World War II and in more recent years Lutheran agencies have strengthened their partnership with congregations. This development grows out of the recognition that both "congregation" and "agency" have unique resources that must be mobilized in every possible way to bring Christ's healing to the lives of all. It has resulted in some new models of partnership. For example, a congregation sponsors a group home for the developmentally disabled. In partnership with a Lutheran social service agency, they build a home on their property or purchase a suitable home nearby, arrange for its management by the agency, and then involve themselves in all the functional activities necessary to the normalization of life for the developmentally disabled. In so doing, the congregation performs a holistic ministry.

A congregation sponsors a meals-on-wheels program for the at-home elderly. In partnership with a Lutheran home for the aged, they utilize their facilities and numerous volunteers who in delivering a nutritious meal also deliver a message of love and care to many elderly people in their apartments and homes.

A congregation provides day care for the children of a working parent or parents. In partnership with a Lutheran agency that provides professional guidance, the congregation uses its parish education facility during the week, manages the program, and ministers to the developmental needs of the children in its care.

A congregation responds to troubled persons and families in its parish and community by offering counselling services. In partnership with a Lutheran agency, the congregation arranges for and supports a professional counsellor and possibly a network of trained volunteer counsellors. It performs a healing ministry.

From these and other models of partnership we could draw a number of observations, but for sake of brevity let these suffice as examples:

1. Our social ministry agencies enable congregations to more fully use their Christian potential for health and healing ministry.
2. Our agencies, homes, and institutions enable congregations to access professional and financial resources not otherwise available to them.
3. An agency provides the congregation with supportive services that it needs to sustain its ministry.
4. Congregations actively involved in health and healing ministry invigorate the life and mission of the Church and its agencies of social ministry. They provide the impetus for new models of partnership.

We are happily discovering that both "agency" and "congregation" are resources for health and healing and that in their partnership they maximize their unique resources in a more holistic ministry.

President Bob Zimmer's statement that Wheat Ridge will do all in its power to impact Lutheran congregations with a renewed challenge and mandate for health and healing in the spirit of Jesus Christ is therefore most welcome.

May Christ's spirit lead us to personally commit ourselves to health and healing in His Name—in His congregation—in His Church.

Dr. John A. Murdock

CHAPTER XI

A Brief Survey of International Health Work

by John A. Murdock

When the United States and other nations were growing in the Industrial Revolution they began a part of the mission movement. Medical missions were an important part of their effort.

Sometimes the medical mission workers preceded the evangelists and teachers. What they were doing was no less threatening to established ways in those countries where they went. To north India, women sent other women who were physicians to give medical care to Moslem women. Those Moslem women were not being treated by the male physicians of their own country.

The usual pattern was to bring the institutional form familiar to the missionaries—the hospital—so buildings like those in Dubuque and Seattle and Jacksonville were put up in Brindaban and Stanleyville. By today's standards they were rather simple facilities, but they were very different from the worlds into which they were introduced.

We must note for later reference that the hospital was never by itself—unaccompanied by education or other efforts.

What was the reason and the context for this mission work? Perhaps mission efforts never are separate from other events in the lands from which they come. American missionaries, for instance, took something of America to the lands to which they went. This is true today as it was true yesterday.

They were the effects of "Manifest Destiny," of nineteenth century capitalism, of the energies of a young and thriving nation. While the desire was "to convert the heathen"—or some other phrase—there was also the desire to make life more pleasant for other human beings. In fact, some missionaries may have wanted one part of that idea and others may have wanted another part. Some of the medical mission workers were not necessarily evangelists but saw healing as an important part of the Gospel by itself.

The missionary groups made health services available to people at little or no cost. They focused upon the poorest of the poor. They certainly did not set up shop in the most convenient places, but they went out into the bush and the villages as well as the cities. With pennies and nickels raised in a thousand different ways in a million different places they provided first rate medical care to people who could not pay.

The people who offered the services were special people. They were

139

dedicated to lives of service. Often they left their homes for the rest of their lives to go to strikingly different worlds where there seemed to be no connections to the rest of the universe. The inconvenience sometimes was accompanied by great danger.

They were symbolized by such famous people as Dr. Livingstone and Dr. Schweitzer. Many of them were formidable people who accomplished much more than their peers who remained at home.

We need to remember that many of the missionaries were not from denominations, but from missionary societies. Someone—a Presbyterian I think—has made a major point of that fact. He said that people got emotionally involved in those societies and in amateurish—"for the love of it"—and enthusiastic ways gave their support. As the work expanded denominations began to institutionalize and regularize it. They included it in their denominational packages and mission societies were replaced by mission boards. Special financial gifts were replaced by percentage amounts of all that was given. He concluded that something was lost in that process because people were put one more step away from the work itself.

Now let's look at some changes between then and now. The changes include the following: Movements have become institutions; local governments have become more active in most areas; the understandings of medicine and health have changed; availability of all resources has changed; the effects of population upon resources continue to be overwhelming.

The institutionalization of medical mission work affected the "sending" countries but it also had its effect on the other end of the line. The hospitals often grew into very large facilities and sometimes they became separate from other mission work. They took on lives of their own.

Local governments interacted with the mission work. Sometimes they took over management. Other times they adopted a national health program and that affected the mission program. Governments began to say things about how much money was spent and how money was spent and what priorities should be. The result was that the "foreign" flavor of the mission work began to be replaced by "local" flavor.

Within the "sending" countries there came to be a different understanding of medicine and health. We began to see the limitations of medical science and the importance of combining it with many other disciplines and daily practices.

At the same time the most sophisticated medicine became more and more expensive. Recently I read the comment that what historians often overlook is that changes in the practice of medicine are due more often to the way things are done than to brilliant ideas. For instance, only in 1896 was a safe and effective way of measuring blood pressure perfected. What an effect that had! Then X-Ray technology had a similar effect. The most recent in that sequence is the CAT-scanner. Without regard to the brilliant ideas of a doctor or medical institution the practice of medicine changes under their feet. And changes often mean more expense.

The expenses of medical mission work have strained the resources that are available. In this paper I will not debate whether more money *should* be available. The fact is that as the churches send less money to medical mission work the hospitals have to turn more and more to patients who are able to pay for services. In some cases hospitals that were created to serve the poor now serve fewer and fewer of them.

The hospitals find it very difficult to keep up with the costs of expensive hardware and medicines. Those hospitals and clinics without electricity also have the problem of keeping medicines fresh.

Human resources are just as much a problem. In a country like ours we find fewer people who want to be gone from home and hearth for a lifetime. We also find more nations with trained personnel of their own. Many programs to which United States churches relate may have no United States personnel around. But many nations do not have enough trained personnel from any source to operate their health care system. May we footnote this observation for later attention.

As all of these changes were taking place, people interested in international health work began to ask whether there were better ways to provide services. Let me use questions to express the ideas. The questions would include the following:

> Is medicine the complete answer to better health; what role does each person have in his/her own health; can we afford health for all; are there more cost-efficient ways to provide health services?

Out of those questions came the concept of primary health care (PHC). In recent years the idea was promoted by the Christian Medical Commission. They then interested the World Health Organization in the idea. Let me begin by saying that PHC cannot be defined before I try to give a limited definition.

To begin with, it is not primary *medical* care. It has to be more than that. You will recall that in my early descriptions I said that mission hospitals never were alone. Missionaries taught something about public health even if they did not know they were doing it. Toilets, hand washing, boiling of water, simple nutritional habits, reducing or eliminating some habits that are potentially dangerous, all are health measures. In some parts of Africa even government public health officials have difficulty getting people to boil drinking water because they associate the practice with Christianity and they are not Christians.

Now we believe that treating a person's disease is not enough. Even giving a shot to immunize against the disease is not enough. Why not help the people to clean up the unsanitary conditions that contribute to contagion? That may not involve hypodermic needles and scalpels and X-Ray units, but paved roads and jobs and clean water and many other non-medical items.

PHC is community-based rather than hospital-based. It comes out of the felt needs of the people. That means that someone must go out to the people to find out what they feel their needs to be.

PHC attempts to use appropriate technology. What good is a cobalt unit where there is no electricity? There are other more subtle examples of appropriate technology.

PHC also may use indigenous healing methods and practitioners as part of its program.

For these and other reasons PHC was not an idea that was welcomed by everyone in mission medicine. Some people thought that it was a radical idea that made no practical sense and that health care would suffer from what they saw as downgrading.

That conflict of views has been bitter and long-lasting. Since I stand in working relationships with people on both sides of the issue I have been bothered by the non-productivity of the argument. As I went to meetings and seminars on international health I found that the same people were always there (or the same organizations), and the same people always were absent.

Since I had the feeling that a synthesis of ideas is becoming possible, we offered a symposium on international health in January. We brought together people from traditional sending and receiving countries, practitioners, academicians and bureaucrats. We had Presbyterians and United Methodists and Lutherans and Southern Baptists and Seventh-Day Adventists and all sorts of people.

We said when we invited people that we would make no attempt to persuade anyone on any point. Instead we wanted to raise the key questions and hear their answers within the context of the theme, "How Do the Churches See Their Future Roles in International Health?" We are publishing the proceedings and I will see that the Foundation gets a copy.

The results were significant. Some older members reminded us that PHC under other names was being practiced decades ago—and it worked. People on opposite sides of the question admitted that both sides were important. One prominent speaker said that he was not opposing the hospitals, but was calling only for a balance in the methods that are used to deliver health services.

That seems to be an eminently sensible approach. The symposium gave us strong evidence of the fusing of two ideas. Hospital-oriented people said that hospitals were not complete until they reached out into the communities; PHC-oriented people said that a general hospital was needed for comprehensive secondary and tertiary levels of care.

You might also be interested to know that throughout three days of discussions all of the persons named the name of Christ as the reason for their work.

Now let us talk for a few moments about the extreme difficulties of health care financing. We will talk in the context of myth in medicine but the problem exists everywhere.

Preventive care is an effective way to improve health status but many still prefer strictly curative hospital-based health care. Why then do so many still prefer curative care to the exclusion of PHC? There appear to be at least four

142

reasons—1. We respond more to pressing need than to later needs. 2. People want health care when they're sick not when they are well. 3. Preventive care is not always seen as "health care." 4. Better educated people already practice preventive medicine themselves.

One of the problems with health care financing is that no one has a formula that tells us how much nations should spend on health care. A formula is needed by every nation. In the absence of such information how can nations plan their health care programs and how can churches relate to those plans? One popular means of analysis is to compare health care costs among societies. The method is not very useful since too many factors, including monetary rates, are not similar or comparable.

Only one overall study ever has been made and it took nine years, from 1958 to 1967. Even then it probably could not have been done without the backing of an organization like World Health Organization. It showed that the poorest nations spent about 3% of their income on health services and the richer nations tended to spend higher percentages as their incomes went up.

One of the most comprehensive national health care systems is in Great Britain. Almost 85% of all of their health care expenses are in the national health plan, and they also control wages for personnel so they have almost full control of health care cost increases. With that control they have held costs at about 6% of their national income. By contrast our costs have gone from about 6% of our income in the 60's to more than 8% in the late seventies. Our increase was caused in part by widespread use of private insurance which reduces the interest of the person receiving services in controlling the costs of those services.

Nations need to be able to see their health care expenditures in the proper light. For a health economist, health care to restore or maintain health status is considered consumption, while health care to increase public health status is considered investment. For all the lack of glamor and altruism, helping a nation to see its health care costs as investment may help them to devote more money to health care.

PHC has not been talked about often enough from the point of view of financial support. In nearly all cases PHC is supported by general taxes or by charity and either one is too limited. More attention needs to be given to community support and the use of indigenous or traditional medicine.

Financial support of health care needs to be included as we review health care in several representative countries.

India—is providing the trained personnel for its hospitals. The national wealth is growing but so is the population. With 80% of the population living in the villages, the fair distribution of health resources is difficult. More than half of the national health budget still is spent in the cities.

Churches and government are stressing development and health. Among many projects is the famous one at Jamkhed run by Mabelle and Raj Arole. The project emphasizes clean water, economic development and education. The problem is in sustaining a good project for a long period of time. Sometimes it seems that the planet is littered with the remains of good ideas for development programs that had short life-spans and affected only a relatively few people. The continuing question is whether those experimental programs tell us anything that is applicable to an entire nation.

We do know that development and health should go together. Carl Taylor spoke of a program of community health and development at Narangwal. Mortality was reduced by almost half, duration of morbidity of major illnesses reduced by 15-20%, average height of all children in experimental villages increased by 2 cm. and average weight by about a pound, psycho-motor scores increased sharply, practice of family planning tripled. Cost effectiveness calculations showed the integrated programs gave the benefits of categorical programs in the same area, but with only slightly more cost when compared to any one categorical program. It had two to three times the cost effectiveness of single purpose programs in achieving family planning practice. In keeping with the concern for social justice the program searched out those who were at greatest risk, preferentially reaching the poorest segments.

Costs of all services was $2 per capita per year. The richer villages in the Punjab could afford that kind of cost but poorer villages could not. Therefore other programs using more community health workers and various economies gave the same results for about $.75 per person per year.

Some of the hospitals in India are very large and complex. The ones related to the churches usually are involved in extensive community health work and PHC. That development is very encouraging for the future.

South Korea—South Korea also has found that economic development alone can improve health to a large extent. The last twenty years were given over to development, and health received a very low priority, never receiving more than 1% of the national budget. However, during that period life expectancy increased from 55 years to 70 years, infant death rates went down from 90 per thousand live births to less than 30, and non-infectious causes replaced infectious diseases as the leading causes of death. Malaria, once rampant, almost disappeared. During that time personal income rose from $70 to $1270.

Now there is a new rural community development program called Saemaul-Undong. It has helped to redistribute wealth to the poorest villages. It began as a government effort that later succeeded through voluntary community effort. Health improved despite only minimal health care efforts.

There are some church related programs in Korea including Yonsei Medical School, which receives no government money.

The nation has other hospitals, nearly all in cities of 50,000 persons and above, and they are under-utilized. South Korea started a new national health insurance plan recently. It is run by private insurance companies with premiums set by the government.

China—We cannot talk about the world without including China. It is best known for barefoot doctors, who are only paramedics with limited training. The more complete story is that China completely restructured its health care system during the 1950s. It has health stations but they must be supported

144

locally. A few major hospitals and some national health programs—such as mother and child health programs—receive national taxes but nothing else does. Probably China spends about 3 to 4% on its health care. Barefoot doctors are paid for prevention at the same pay rate received by factory workers.

Nepal—The population growth is not so high as in nearby India but that is due largely to a high infant mortality rate. As that rate is brought down Nepal could face the same kind of population problems that India has faced. Nepal is a poor country. It is not open to religious proselytizing. The medical mission workers are there through United Mission to Nepal. The nation's health care program is reasonably well-balanced because the King gives planning direction to the work and gives some fairness of distribution to services, scarce as they are.

Africa is so large that we see a variety of situations. Kenya has a strong economy and that is reflected in rather comprehensive health services. Zaire has a faltering economy and out in the countryside mission hospitals are having great difficulty even getting supplies. In other countries some people use the term "fourth world." By that they mean that the situation seems to give no promise of great improvement in the near future. Included in a list of such countries would be Guinea-Bissau, Lesotho, and Malawi.

Those are countries that may have had about two dollars per person per year in recent years for all health services. By the time one hypodermic shot is given to each person much of that budget already has been used up.

Tanzania—The country suffers from slow transportation and communication. It has had serious water needs for some time and wells are now being dug throughout the country. However, much of the water that is found is too heavily mineralized to be generally useful.

The government has taken over two church hospitals, one at the church's request. They now have fifteen designated district hospitals with two more being built. There is a great need for trained local staff at all levels, especially mid-management, technicians, and doctors. Discussions have been reopened between government and church on health care. There is an emphasis on decentralizing the health services with the building of dispensaries throughout the country that have no beds for in-patient care. Special attention is being given to TB and leprosy.

Malawi—First opened to the West by Livingstone in 1859, the country provides 40% of its care through 138 Christian hospitals, health centers, and dispensaries. Those hospitals belong to the Private Health Association of Malawi (PHAM). The nation has 502 hospitals and dispensaries, but only 127 doctors. Five percent of the health budget goes to PHAM. There is a fifteen year plan to have care facilities within five miles of any person in the country and to place an emphasis on mother and child care and care for children under five. One-third of all children die before age five, and the life expectancy at birth is only forty-five years.

Water-borne diseases, measles, and malnutrition comprise the leading causes of death. There are one million cases of malaria per year but no national anti-malaria program. The national health budget is now about $2.60 per person per year. There is a shortage of trained personnel. Hospitals get about one-fourth of their income from government. A recent wage bill has raised wages thirty-two percent. Several hospitals are in serious financial difficulty.

Botswana—The most frequent types of diseases are TB, respiratory diseases, and skin diseases. Life expectancy at birth is about forty-four years. Immunization programs look good in Botswana with BCG being given to 90% of the population, small-pox 80%, DPT and polio 52%, and measles 56%. Family planning is growing slowly so that in 1978 10% of women were using contraceptives, up from 6% in 1976. National priorities are placed upon PHC, health training, employment, and health programs including health education and services for persons with handicapping conditions. There is increasingly good coordination of the national health work. In the mission hospitals there is not one national doctor. Training of personnel is receiving national attention. There is a great need for libraries and educational materials.

In the areas served by Pan-American Health Organization (PAHO)—South America, Central America, and the Caribbean—life expectancies vary widely from as little as 50 years at birth to as much as 72 years. Infant mortality rates range from almost 20 to 160 per 100,000 population. The region could have five hundred million (500,000,000) inhabitants by the turn of the century. In these nations and in all of the nations of the world many governments are putting more money into their national health budgets. But the ultimate question is not how much money a country budgets for health care but how much it actually spends on health care, and how much it spends in its most remote villages and among its poorest people.

In Central America most present day health services were started by missionaries and most of them still center upon curative medicine. There is movement toward the training of village health workers however. Costa Rica has a new PHC program, with 34 health posts and 4 centers built with community help to serve 81,000 persons in a 1350 square kilometer area. They emphasize not just medicine and health but also "human promotion."

Guatemala has a new association of community health services of Guatemala for 150 health-oriented non-governmental organizations, seventy-nine percent of which are church-related. They aim to provide educational services, a central pharmacy, and to study traditional medicine. In Guatemala church-related community health programs are finding great success in remote mountain areas.

In Haiti there is a planned rural health center in a highly populated but isolated and unserved northern area. The center is designed to serve 20,000 people with training of female village health workers, male community development workers, traditional birth attendants, and herbalists. They will have health education, nutrition, family planning, agricultural development, and curative medicine as their programs.

In remote and mountainous Argentina Dr. Monsalvo is finding considerable success in serving Indian tribes.

146

The South Pacific also should be included in our brief review.

Papua New Guinea—There is rather extensive ·health coverage and emphasis on increasing quality. National workers are being trained to take over from Australians. The United Church has some work, limited to health clinics and nursing staffs.

Solomon Islands—The islands have very limited facilities with one hospital in the capital Honiara, Guadalcanal. Clinics are scattered and poorly equipped and staffed. The United Church has a good hospital in Munda near the center of the island nation. It has a New Zealand doctor. There is a clinic at Sege, but it is not of very high quality.

New Hebrides—Under British and French rule medical facilities were rather good in Vila, the capital, but what is offered in the out-islands is very limited. The Presbyterian Church does not have any medical facility with its work there. The Roman Catholics have some limited programs. The opportunity for island health programs is unlimited, especially with British and French leaving the islands.

Fiji—The government has sophisticated medical centers and training programs. There is a modern 400-bed facility which was opened only four years ago. Medical care in the out-islands is very limited. The Methodists have a 75-bed hospital at Ba, but the government has discouraged its growth and upgrading by refusing funds. Since they do not have sufficient budgeted, and have difficulty with government bureaucracies, expatriate personnel are leaving, including many Indian doctors invited from India.

Western Samoa and *Tonga*—Both countries have minimal health services. The big problem is how to deliver services at reasonable cost with qualified personnel to the out-island communities.

Singapore—Singapore has highly sophisticated facilities with highly qualified personnel from both local and foreign sources. It has become a center for Southeast Asia specialties and much of the finest medical work in the area is done in Singapore.

Now that we have looked very briefly at a few third world nations and at least one western nation, we also need to look at Eastern Europe.

When Germany was divided, the churches in the DDR (East Germany) faced a bleak future. Their memberships fell sharply and still are falling. After all, an ambitious person in a Marxist state would not strengthen his or her resumé by showing church membership on it. But while the membership has been falling, the health and welfare work of the church in the DDR has gotten even stronger.

The Diakonisches Innere Mission provides ecumenical leadership for their work. The work includes perhaps the best hospitals in the nation. The physicians have formed an evangelical physician's group. They have strong child-care work, but more and more of that has been taken over by the State. They have several large and good homes for the aged and general programs for older people. They have some of the best care programs and facilities for retarded persons and persons with handicapping conditions.

They talk a great deal about holistic healing and the following observations can be made:

—Biblical training is emphasized so that young "diakonic" (health and welfare) workers will be able to pass their knowledge on to others.

—Geriatric training is available by correspondence with an emphasis on the holistic.

—General parish workers also will be training soon by correspondence.

—For the psychologically handicapped a psychotherapeutic ward is available.

—There are psychiatric seminars for family counseling, for those working with drug/alcohol abuse, and for industrial missions. The seminars are for full time and voluntary workers.

They feel that the Church cannot stand apart from "diakonic" services, and they see the Church's saving work and healing work needing to be together.

They point out that a church in a socialist country does not necessarily mean that the church is socialist. The future of the Church in any society does not depend upon the benevolence of the state. The future of the Church was determined at the Resurrection. The Kingdom will come, and religious forms will appear that will allow the Church to live. They believe that the future is with their health and welfare work.

That is very interesting to me. What happens to a church when it is reduced in membership and cut off from its earlier work with other nations? Does it die quickly and quietly? Not in Eastern Europe. It moves strongly into helping and healing work.

I have tried to give you a limited background of medical mission work and then a quick overview of contemporary situations. I cannot resist giving you a brief summary that displays nearly all of my biases in this area—

1. Health care services must be seen as a matter of social justice, and any imbalance in service should be in favor of the poor—most of whom do not have regular access to permanent health care services.

2. While health care is first the responsibility of each nation, many nations are unable to organize effective health care work. The flow of resources must be increased from the richer nations and those resources must get to the people.

148

3. The churches of the nations with resources still have major roles to play. They may be able to give money, they may be able to give educational help, or they may be able to give materials.

4. A minimum of health care services should be available to all people, as called for in the World Health Organization theme of "Health For All By the Year 2000."

5. PHC is an effective tool to help deliver at least minimal services, but it must be used in a comprehensive system.

6. The churches must help to redefine "development" so that it means not just a rising line on an economic graph but so that it means clean water, better nutrition, and better health care.

7. People who are to receive services should help decide the nature of those services.

8. Educational programs should be developed to help promote health.

9. Local congregations can play important roles in healing.

As we have attempted to provide healing in the name of Christ, we have developed several different institutional forms. One that is overlooked is the congregation. The congregation cannot carry out its ministry of healing simply by supporting specialized institutions that provide health care services.

Congregations can provide direct service health care programs. Those programs can include health services, residential services, counseling, and spiritual healing.

The congregation may also play a role in health education. It can provide information for church members that warn us against dangerous personal habits and it can encourage healthier habits. It can provide information about basic sanitation and hygiene.

The congregation also can help us to find human environments that are most conducive to health and wholeness.

The congregation has not carried out its complete ministry until it has engaged in programs of healing such as those noted above.

Many of the most important questions being dealt with in all parts of the world today impinge upon questions of health. The Church has a most important role to play in that area.

CHAPTER XII

Task Group Reports

TASK GROUP 1.

Topic: The place of health and healing in the parish.

Report: *Message from Yahara*

We greet you, healers of God in an ailing world, in the name of Christ, the Healer!

God has made known His mission of healing for the brokenness of His world and His people. He reveals this mission especially in the life and ministry, death and resurrection of Jesus Christ. (Isaiah 53:5: "But he was wounded for our transgressions, he was bruised for our iniquities; upon him was the chastisement that made us whole, and with his stripes we are healed." Luke 4:18-19: "The Spirit of the Lord is upon me, because he has anointed me to preach good news to the poor. He has sent me to proclaim release to the captives and recovering of sight to the blind, to set at liberty those who are oppressed, to proclaim the acceptable year of the Lord." Luke 9:2: "And he sent them out to preach the kingdom of God and to heal.") God has given us His gift of salvation and wholeness, and calls His people into His healing mission. To every Christian congregation, God's healing community, he says: "As my Father has sent me, so send I you." (John 20:21)

The community of God's people is a broken community, living in a broken world. But at the same time it is a healed and healing community. This brokenness, which yearns for healing, is both individual and corporate. Tragically, we know the effects of brokenness, such as injury, disease, and incapacity, conflict and tension with self and others, pollution and abuse, threat of war and calamities, imprisonment by racism and disenfranchisement, and imposed philosophies and life styles. Healing in this life is never complete. Yet, paradoxically, wholeness of life is experienced in the midst of pain and suffering. Those who suffer can lay claim to healing in spite of their infirmities, through the peace which comes from God and through those who love, care, and support. We share in the suffering of Christ and "by His stripes we are healed."

God proclaims: "I love you. I have demonstrated to you in so many ways how much I desire your life in spite of how broken you are. Accept that love in your whole being, and let it go forth from you, and through you, to my people wherever they are and in whatever condition. Let my healing grace operate through your life to my people in every circumstance of need. Lead my people to wholeness of life and ultimately to me."

TASK GROUP 2.

Topic: A process for developing an effective parish program.

We felt it necessary to redefine the task, i.e., "to construct a planning process for an effective parish program in healing ministry."

In order to develop a planning process, we deemed it necessary to state the goal we would envision congregations having as follows: WE ARE SEEKING AN ACTION PROCESS ENABLING LOCAL CONGREGATIONS TO BE CHRISTIAN COMMUNITIES, EXPERIENCING, ENJOYING, AND SHARING HEALTH AND HEALING."

Before proceeding with the methodology of process, the assumption needs to be stated: "We need to keep our eyes firmly fixed on Christ, the Healer, as we work through the process—for there can be no experience, enjoyment, or sharing of healing apart from Him!" A further assumption is the need for a real sense of community/togetherness in the congregation. The process will always anticipate that sense though it may not always be specifically stated. Implementation of the process will vary from parish to parish.

I. STRATEGIES FOR DEVELOPING CONGREGATIONAL INTEREST
   A. Provide information; resources from Wheat Ridge Symposium and related material; health information; theological perspective; cooperative efforts with Synodical and/or District Social Ministry Committees or equivalent.
   B. Affirm healing and health that is presently happening in congregation.
   C. Developing recognition of a need for a more effective health and healing ministry.

II. TRAINING EXPERIENCES
   A. Workshopping with leadership groups.
   B. Development of community/togetherness among leadership group.

III. ENVISIONING BY LEADERSHIP GROUP
   A. Recognizing brokenness and disease
   B. Envisioning a healing and healthful community
   C. Envisioning via dialog of neighborhood and congregational persons
   D. Identifying resources for fulfilling the vision, i.e.,
      1. Congregation
      2. Neighborhood
      3. Church at large

151

IV. EXPANDING OWNERSHIP OF THIS MINISTRY TO ENTIRE CON-
GREGATION
  A. Workshopping with additional groups (See II A and III)
  B. Possibility of every member contact

V. DEVELOPING ACTION GOALS
  A. Integrate total process into worship and education ministries
  B. Developing measurable, achievable goals
  C. Consider using "models" such as the 9 models presented at the Wheat
     Ridge Symposium, March 10-14, 1980
  D. Consider development of new models for effective health and healing
     ministries

VI. IMPLEMENTATION OF GOALS
  A. Assign responsibilities
  B. Develop time-line

VII. EVALUATION AS AN ONGOING PROCESS

Task Force II recommends that all participants having access to the decision
making leadership of Lutheran Synods, Districts, and National Church bodies
memorialize said bodies to foster implementation of ministries for health and
healing in local congregations.

TASK GROUP 3.

Topic: Criteria for evaluation of the effectiveness of existing and new model
       ministries.

EVALUATION OF PARISH HEALTH AND HEALING MINISTRY.

I. *PREAMBLE*

The purpose of evaluation is to estimate the worth of a particular ministry,
based on its goals and objectives; it should be viewed as adding value to work
undertaken, an acknowledgement of what the ministry has contributed to the
health of persons, parishes, and communities.
    Evaluation of proposed or existing programs should be periodic and ongo-
ing, done by those people who have agreed in advance to the goals, objectives,
and criteria for evaluation. The purpose of this evaluation process is not necessarily to bring outside judgment upon the program but rather an exercise in
self-evaluation and of systematic review.
    The basic questions to be answered in an evaluation are (1) What is to be
the changed state because this program has been started?; and (2) How have
people changed because this effort was begun?

The goals and objectives should be set in advance, with a maximum participation of both the congregation and the community to their mutual benefit. Let them be specific and clear.

II. *CRITERIA*
Evaluations "add value" to programs when they answer such questions as:
1. Was the ministry developed from identified and demonstrated health needs?
2. Was the ministry developed in a broad-based way: e.g. by individuals, committees, and a parish at large; by consumers, providers, and consultants?
3. Were program objectives clearly stated and specific to the demonstrated needs?
4. Were the means—quantitative (most preferable), descriptive (less preferable), personal judgment (least preferable)—and sources of evaluation developed during planning for the ministry?
5. Were resources for implementing the ministry gathered from a broad base: e.g. parishioners, parishioners who are also health professionals, community consultants; church and community health agencies and institutions; church and community financial resources?
6. Did the ministry do what it was intended to do? To what extent? Did its developers aim too high? Too low? About right? Did it have sufficient resources? Why or why not?
7. Was the expenditure of moneys, time, and effort worth it?
8. Should the activity be continued, expanded, suspended, or otherwise revised?

III. *BASES FOR EVALUATION*
The following questions are offered as aids in evaluating parish involvement in health and healing ministry:
1. *Individual involvement.* How have people changed their involvement in healing relationships in the parish and beyond? How does this compare to a year ago?
2. *People equipped for health ministry.* How have members become better equipped during the past year to serve as "health ministers"?
3. *Improvement in personal health.* How have behavior modification programs improved health in the parish community? How many people participate?
4. *Coordination of resources.*
   a. How has the parish integrated resources and services of community health agencies as a part of its ministry? How does this compare with one year ago?
   b. How has the parish improved understanding and cooperation with the medical community? Were there joint projects? Were there bilateral education programs?

TASK GROUP 4.

Topic: Future Direction

SPECULATIONS ON FUTURE CHANGES

Demographic
Stratification of society will continue and intensify.
Changing patterns will include: increasing density of population, reduced mobility because of the energy shortage, return to the urban situation, and changes in suburbia, ethnic mixing.

Technological
Continuing communications and knowledge explosions.
Technological displacement and work pattern changes.
Increased specialization.
Accumulation of hazardous wastes of civilization.
Electronic church as continuing challenge to old patterns.

Political
Increasing power of multi-national conglomerates, despite interdependence of the entire world.
Concentration of power with attendant struggle in national health care versus personal care.
Shifts in church-state relationships.
Powerlessness to effect change and rising consumer advocacy.
Taxpayers' revolts.
Increased power of the elderly and other low-power groups.
Increased recognition that the resources of the earth—food, mineral, water— are limited.
Urban revitalization.
Military crises, conventional and nuclear.

Economic
Increased stratification—the poor becoming poorer and the rich richer.
Increasing responsibility for aged, unemployable, and marginally employable groups.
Global interdependence struggling with power of the conglomerates.
Consumer manipulation, e.g., advertising.
Demands for smaller residences and according shift in living arrangements.
Unemployment, inflation, shifting tax base, insurance for various purposes.
Mass transportation arising from uneconomic private transportation.
Increasing costs of medical care.

154

The preceding remarks lead to some changes in the *Quality of Life:*

Global consciousness, sharper in some cases, superficial in many.
Educational changes, with more emphasis upon technological skills, attendant decline in public education, strong currents of anti-intellectualism, scholarliness declining.
Revolt against obsolescence and waste.
Struggle for more adequate uses of leisure time, with attendant revision of work ethic.
Changing values and attitudes toward them; hedonism, especially demand for release from pain.
Increasing moral and ethical problems as technology affects many options.
Loss of privacy with increasing living density.
Changing life styles affecting family and church.
Increasing feeling of powerlessness.
New understanding of the meaning of health.
Changing attitudes toward the elderly as wisdom resource for society.

The impact of these trends can and will be seen in some of the following ways, suggesting a generalized *stress syndrome:*

Despair, false hopes, fantasy.
Stress related disease states—hypertension, headache, cardio-vascular disease, ulcers.
Diffuse anxiety and fear of the unknown, i.e., ''Is there any future?''
Obsessive compulsive work, workaholism.
Increased sense of isolation and alienation.

The preceding stress syndromes give rise to the following paradoxical *behavioral responses,* which can arise from purely human reactions, outside the Christian ethics.

Increased substance abuse, e.g. drugs, alcohol, tobacco, food—vs.—appreciation and appropriate care for the body.
Exploitative sexuality—vs.—renewed understanding of appropriate sexual expression.
Family disintegration—vs.—renewed commitment and support to integrity of the family in various forms.
Increased violence—vs.—positive use of power.
Retreat into ''entertainment leisure''—vs.—creative use of leisure.
Revolutionary actions leading to negative social change—vs.—revolutionary counter actions leading to positive social change.
Self-gratification, retreat from moral and ethical values—vs.—greater concern for morality and compassion.

Retreat into privatized spirituality—vs.—use of religion and faith to motivate creative compassionate response.

Self-protective life style, including greed, "me first," narcissism—vs.—concern for others.

Responses of the Church

1. The first response of the church is to recognize and confess its complete complicity in the situation to which it is addressing itself. Consumer pressure and manipulation are *our* responsibility, not *theirs*. Narcissism, despair, anxiety, alienation are ours. Any argument about lesser blame is to deny the prophetic truth of our fault, our grievous fault as individuals, institutions, community. Without this confession and a plea for forgiveness, there can be no effective response to either the present or the future.

2. Secondly, we are called as Christians to be involved in the struggle for the health and well-being of society and the individual in the midst of all the weakness and failure of which we are part. Our strength lies not in greater wisdom but in mutual encouraging that follows Christ, limping and lagging, but still following. In this understanding we can anticipate some of the following roles for the local parish:

a) Increasing importance of the church as source for personalized human interaction (priesthood of all believers).

b) Increasing role of the church as value guide for the religious community as well as general society.

c) Need for assisting persons in values clarification in dealing with increasing ethical dilemmas, e.g. right-to-die, pacemaker ethics.

d) Greater need for articulation of positive realistic hope.

e) Increasing role of information and referral to various self-help groups whether or not sponsored or supported by the church. Probably increasing role in being called to initiate and support such groups in various ways.

f) Increasing role as "practitioner" in various areas of health care and promotion of well-being (e.g., wholistic health center).

g) Increasing need to be advocate, to enter into an advocacy role for various types of health and preventive programs.

h) Need to articulate a theology that sustains a sense of self-sacrifice, courage even through defeat, hope in the face of hopelessness (theology of the cross) rather than a theology that promises easy victories or offers false security (theology of glory—cheap grace).

PARISH NEIGHBORHOOD SYSTEMS CHART

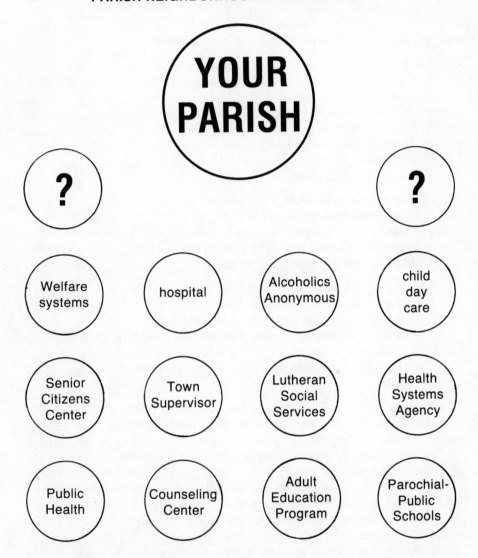

Each of the above systems are some of the ministries, or services which exist in the Community. Cut out each circle and place it in the above circle, away from it, or somewhere in between. You will be able to see how your church relates to the above or other services. An AA chapter with no relationship to your parish or people would be outside the circle. A day care center serving churched and unchurched would be somewhere on the line. Have FUN but consider what might need to happen to make your ministry more inclusive!

TASK GROUP 5.

Topic: The parish as a place within which to examine and relate to larger needs in the larger context.

Community Health Systems can provide to the parish:

A. Stable, ongoing resources for the development of parish programs
   1. Technical skills and professional competence for programs
   2. Expertise for training volunteers, etc.
   3. Methods for accountability
   4. Programs to provide needed information
   5. Ability to assess community needs
   6. Experimental models that might be used by the parish
   7. Funds for health programs

B. Programs and services which can be used by parishioners
   1. Professional medical/technical services
   2. Senior citizen centers
   3. Financial assistance for health care through welfare funds
   4. Housing/residential care for elderly

C. Ongoing opportunities for Christian services
   1. Exercise of health-related vocation
   2. Volunteer services in local health institutions
   3. Presenting a Christian witness through one's concern for community health care
   4. Providing space within the church building for community health programs

The Role of the Parish in Influencing the Delivery of Health Care
The church provides a unique dimension to health care which no other segment can: the spiritual component. It is unique among those holistic healers at large in that it is concerned about and does care for the afflicted, the broken, the disenfranchised, and the well.

The individual parish can provide new ministry to its people. It can offer a forum for the discussion of the health needs of the members of the parish and the community at large. In a period of rapid change the parish can encourage its members to speak out in this area to identify unmet needs, breakdowns in service delivery, and to stimulate the development of alternative models. It can educate members to become intelligent consumers.

The scientific, medical community appears receptive to learning about new and more effective ways to deal with that portion of our sick population whose illnesses are related to problems of the human spirit and condition.

These efforts on the part of the parish need to reflect our belief that God created the whole person, not just his soul. It has a further obligation to formulate the message of the continuing renewal of the whole person. Accepting and treating our bodies as a gift from God must be given more public statement.

As God has given unique gifts to individuals, He also gives unique gifts to individual parishes. Just as no one individual can provide for all health care needs, neither can an individual parish.

The parish may provide the opportunity for its members, both individually and collectively to discover and practice responsible health maintenance.

Caring for one's health includes the responsibility of understanding and becoming involved in the political process through which decisions are made regarding health policy. There are 3 areas where the parish can engage with the community in the political arena.

1. Parish programs are often examples of practical action programs which alter and change the daily living patterns in the community.
2. Demonstrating the ways a Christ-centered life style changes peoples' motivation, values, and thinking.
3. Parishioners are the constituents of political systems which make the decisions affecting the lives of people in the parish and community at large.

The parish can provide an arena to stimulate thought, encourage discussion, develop models of health care to meet human and spiritual needs and influence the implementation of health policies. A rudimentary list of some present possibilities include:

1. Engaging in discussions with present providers of health care
2. Become a resource for the promotion of preventive health care programs for its members
3. Become a center to deliver health care for unmet needs in the neighborhood
4. Teach its members the prudent use of existent medical facilities
5. Develop self help and support groups to enable people to face their illnesses creatively and as Christians
6. Emphasize the cost-effectiveness of parish programs
7. Groom members to participate in health policy making boards

TASK GROUP 6.

Topic: Implications for worship.

As a task force on worship we conclude:

1. Worship is a healing experience
2. Worship is one important resource for healing that is complementary to other God-given resources

3. We need to heighten this awareness in congregations and help them develop healing worship aids

We recommend that the Wheat Ridge Foundation develop and/or provide a resource kit of health, healing, and worship which would include:

1. A sensitive examination of existent worship forms together with aids to enhance their fullest use. This would specifically include:
   a. An illustrative and instructive cassette tape to help the worship leader present the liturgy in a warm and caring way
   b. Dividing the worship service (particularly the Eucharist) into its integral parts helping us to see the many opportunities for interpersonal relations (e.g. passing the peace, verbal sharing, intercessory prayers, psalm readings, testimonies)

2. A compendium of pastoral aids including:
   a. A gathering of appropriate scriptural portions on health and healing together with textual studies of at least some of the passages
   b. A collection of special prayers for a broad range of human circumstances that affirm health or call for healing
   c. A variety of services for special occasions and situations, for instance, informal worship gatherings (e.g. nursing homes and hospitals), lay services, emergency baptisms.

3. Special liturgies to be used in various auxiliaries of the congregation and on special occasions
   a. A Sunday school and/or parochial school series of short sermons on health and healing, together with practical illustrations
   b. A Lenten series with a health and healing accent
   c. Healing liturgies which illustrate and/or include anointing, affirmation of baptism, foot washing, and other expressions of the servant role.

4. A special series of three or four congregational worship services celebrating health and affirming healing. For instance, healing of family relationships, physical healing, emotional healing, the resolution of social tensions.

5. A collection of worship aids such as bulletins, inserts, banners, new hymns, chancel dramas, and the use of creative art forms (e.g. visual aids, mime and "clowning," dancing, light shows) which will support all of the above.

We do not expect the Wheat Ridge Foundation to produce by itself all of the above, but that it also encourage publishing houses and other agencies to participate in this venture and promote the entire matter through jurisdictions of the Lutheran churches and their gatherings, colleges and seminaries of the various synods, and other appropriate means.

TASK GROUP 7.

Topic: Implications for education.

Report: *HEALTH AND HEALING WE TEACH*

Statement of Purpose: Education about health and healing in the parish would reflect the healing and teaching ministry of Jesus. We accept the broken nature of humanity, including the pervasive presence of physical and emotional infirmity, social inequities, and evil in society. Our efforts are to enlighten and extend the encompassing love that has been given to us in Christ. Any goal for better health education has validity only in this context.

Directions

1. Teaching the theology of healing
2. Teaching people how to minister
3. Supervising/Maintaining physical health
4. Psychological and emotional health
5. Dying and Death
6. Celebrating our physical vitality
7. Our bodies
8. Consciousness Raising Beyond the Parish: Global Issues
9. Ethics and decision making in health issues
10. Political/Health Related Issues

Programs

1. To trace the healing power/record of the church
2. (a) Parenting
   (b) Stephens Ministers
   (c) C.P.E. (13 steps)
3. (a) Wellness Kit
   (b) Health Hazard Assessment
   (c) Immunization
   (d) Anti-Smoking
4. (a) Role of Stress
   (b) Depression
5. (a) Existing programs and literature
   (b) Persons who have experienced loss, death
6. (a) Dance/Mime/Sports
   (b) Sexuality

7. (a) Sex Education
   (b) Family Life Enrichment
   (c) Aging Process
8. (a) Data sharing
   (b) Third World Conditions
9. (a) Abortion issues and problems
   (b) Life sustaining technology
   (c) Artificial Insemination
   (d) Genetic Problems
10. (a) Public Policy Issues—(National Health Insurance, Military expenditure)

Resources

1. Bible study/church history
2. Pastor; self-help buddies
3. (a) Sunday School
   (b) Health Professionals
4. (a) Pastor
   (b) Health Professionals
5. (a) Pastor
   (b) Health Professionals
   (c) Congregation Members
6. ---
7. ---
8. (a) Returning Missionaries
   (b) Inner city and Third World visits
9. ---
10. ---

Objectives

1. To understand the Gospel in terms of now
2. To have people empathize with others' physical/emotional burdens
3. Sensitization to personal care of the body
4. Basic understanding of emotions
5. (a) To understand the dying process and grief
   (b) To realize the power of Christ
   (c) The importance of faith in dying
6. (a) Celebrate life according to capacity
   (b) Develop an attitude of gratitude for the physical self
7. (a) Better understanding of human growth, development and behavior
   (b) Preparation for parenthood
   (c) Decrease in teenage pregnancy

162

8. (a) To overcome indifference
   (b) To minister to the less fortunate
   (c) To look beyond in the spirit of Christ
9. (a) To achieve value based decisions
10. To set priorities for improving health services

TASK GROUP 9.

Topic: Identifying, maximizing and developing resources.

It is not difficult to identify the resources for health and healing ministries to the parishes. We are impressed by both the number and variety of resources within our reach. What we seem to lack is a focus for developing and using the resources available within our parishes and developing the linkages to outside groups. We wish to present suggestions for developing that focus by discussing guidelines and strategies for identifying, developing and maximizing resources by first considering those within the parish and then those outside the parish. We conclude with an example of a model for utilization of resources within a parish.

I. *RESOURCES WITHIN THE PARISH*
   A. *Identifying*. Identifying resources within the parish is a fairly straightforward task with the scope of the search defined by the mission and policies for health and healing. Identification seems to have two principal thrusts.
      1. Developing a list of resources for health and healing. Examples include the sacraments; religious and health care professionals; ongoing support groups; sick, broken and recovering people; crisis intervention resources; money; voting power; a body of knowledge; newsletters; etc.
      2. Identifying the unique ministries of members
         a. Listing health care professionals in the parish
         b. Compile an aggregate listing of Lutheran health care professionals at the national, district, or synod level
         c. Survey congregations to identify current healing activities.
   B. *Developing*. In order to develop the identified resources in some rational way we suggest that parishes begin with and look to a mission statement for the health and healing ministry.
      1. Use mission statement to develop guidelines or policies concerning:
         a. Scope of ministry (e.g. congregational, geographical neighborhoods, or denominational; crisis intervention, health prevention, long-term followup
         b. System for accountability

163

    c. Criteria for determining focus, such as:
       1) whether or not to phase in the healing ministry. For example a parish may begin with programs or projects that have high probability of success moving into more complex and value-laden activities when the concept is more firmly established
       2) be manageable
       3) have personal, congregational, and societal value
    d. Goal statement regarding the type and variety of people to be involved in serving
    e. consistent with Biblical and religious beliefs and heritage of the parish
  2. Specific Strategies
    a. Continuing education and support for members in healing vocations
    b. Consumer education: consumer rights, strategies and styles for approaching health care providers, basic health care and self-help information, putting people in contact with outside programs
    c. Affirm current healing activities by labeling them as such (vehicles could include church newsletters, Sunday announcements, etc.)
    d. Assign administrative responsibility for health and healing to a person or group
    e. Consciousness raising: problems of health are one of the major problems of our time and are the business of the church
    f. Reconciliation of the stigmatized (e.g. alcoholics, psychiatric patients, handicapped persons, offenders)
       1) help those in need find assistance
       2) help parish members understand the problem and overcome their own feelings of inadequacy in ministering to the person in need

C. *Maximizing/Sustaining*
  1. Give health and healing ministry official status
  2. Provide for support of care providers
  3. Support social rituals that support members (e.g. meals after funerals)

II. *RESOURCES OUTSIDE THE PARISH*
  A. *Identifying*
    1. Those healing agencies/institutions with which the congregation interacts and supports through:
      a. financial commitment
      b. volunteers
      c. employees
      d residents
      e. clients

2. Other community agencies which offer
   a. educational programs
   b. outreach opportunities
   c. free service (i.e. blood pressure checks, etc.)
3. Church related financial resources
   a. foundations
   b. insurance agencies
   c. district/synod mission appeals
4. Theological Schools and Seminaries
5. Government funding sources
   a. grants
   b. cost-reimbursement programs
   c. employment programs (especially for low-income and elderly persons)

B. *Developing*
   1. Establish a "Fellowship of St. Luke"
   2. Develop a "language" for use by Lutheran people in power positions for health advocacy
   3. Expand the theology curriculum regarding health and healing in our seminaries
   4. Actively support risk takers, even in failure
   5. Initiate congregational co-ops and cooperation in health and healing
   6. Contract for specific services from already established providers
   7. Realize the potential for financial assistance
   8. Assertively affirm the servers and services provided.

C. *Maximizing*
   1. Support from Wheat Ridge for "Fellowship of St. Luke"
   2. Advocate for health and healing needs, issues, and awareness
   3. Specifically designate linking people between resources outside the congregation and the congregation
   4. Use existing community structure whenever possible

III. *MODEL OF UTILIZATION OF RESOURCES WITHIN A PARISH*
   A. Parish develop a complete list of members presently involved in health care: both professionals and volunteers in health care
   B. An annual St. Luke's Festival be conducted in the parish for several days in October
      1. worship service could include public affirmation of members involved in health care services as an expression of parish's healing ministry
      2. a seminar be conducted for health care professionals
      3. a congregational event be held to focus on an issue of healing and health of community-wide interest
   C. The parish newsletter contain articles on and lists of members involved in health and healing ministries

165

D. The parish plan and carry out an annual health care project for its members (e.g. CPR training)
E. The parish utilize some of its members in health care to conduct an annual workshop to equip other members for service projects in health care in the community
F. The parish provide opportunity for a small group of concerned people to identify a health care issue, conduct research on the issue, and become an advocate for Christian implications of the issue within the parish and the community (e.g. drugs, patient rights in health care, healing services)

TASK GROUP 10.

Topic: Family and health care.

Preamble

We recognize that families come in all shapes and sizes. There are countless types of and settings for family life. But one thing they all share is the need for identity: the need to tell a story and, out of that story, to develop a self-awareness and a vocation.

In that sense, a family's story which connects it with the past and helps it to focus on the future is an act of healing: a making whole, a stand against fragmentation and reductionism. Consequently it is important that the church provide opportunity and encouragement to people
a. to tell their story
b. to affirm their identity and location within the larger story and tradition of the church; and
c. to assist in the discovery and/or expression of a vocation that grows out of these stories and traditions.
Thus, every family is a story that is being told. We do not view health as an end in itself, but rather, we encourage people and families to seek health "so that"—so that they might fulfill their vocations as Christians.

Family as a Health Care System

We view the family as a health care system for maintaining itself as a functioning unit and sponsoring the personal development and well-being of its members as well as others in the congregation and community. The challenge of the congregation is to help energize that system.

Taking Stock

In order to energize the family system as a health care provider we encourage a systematic review of the congregation and its environment. Answers to the following questions would facilitate an action process:

1. What kinds of family forms are in our church?
2. Do congregational activities focus on only one type of family form?
3. What is the tradition of culture of the congregation? Its judicatory? Its national church body?
4. Do activities affirm people in family or focus only on individuals?
5. Are (your) families interested in promoting wellness and health?
6. What are (your) families doing to promote wellness among family members?
7. How does our congregation minister to the health needs of unique family forms?

Taking Action

We recommend three ways that the congregation might energize its families to take action consistent with the data gathered in the review process. They are: 1) caring through promotion of health; 2) caring in crisis; and 3) caring through ongoing support processes.

Caring Through Promotion of Health

Promotion of health among families in congregations is understood to include an educational and supportive process which enables the family to function effectively to maintain the health of individual members and family as a system. The process may assume the format of a specific educational program to stimulate interest and promote an increased level of health understanding and be made available to members of the community as well as the congregation. Other formats may include pastoral counseling, programs at key developmental points in the family life cycle, worship services, recognizing health goals, social network support to families, and encouragement in prayer and meditation.

Caring in Crisis

We consider the congregation's ability to help the family in crisis situations to be integral to the ministry of healing. We view crisis as an event which upsets the family's equilibrium or usual way of functioning. Crisis presents the dual motifs of danger and opportunity. The goals of caring in crisis may be minimal—to restore functioning to previous capacity—or maximal—to achieve growth and improved patterns of functioning. Congregational efforts may be directed through the pastor's intervention, through a network of volunteers trained to intervene in pain filled situations and through an informal network to offer immediate, tangible services and links to resources. We encourage public celebrational recognition of efforts made in crisis intervention and prayerful response to crises overcome.

We also see the potential for the congregation to help families help themselves as they confront crises.

Caring Through Ongoing Support Process

We perceive that an ongoing supportive ministry is necessary to complement the health and the healing process of the family in the congregation. It is vital that families and the congregation be sensitized to human hurts and encouraged in the compassionate response in daily activities. Systems supportive of families include creating opportunities for families to come together in a variety of sharing experiences.

Roster

of persons attending the symposium "Health and Healing: Ministry of the Church" held at Yahara Center, Madison, WI, March 10-14, 1980.

Dr. Adrian L. Bacarisse, parish pastor/chaplain, Shreveport, LA

The Rev. Donald W. Balster, parish pastor, Hinsdale, IL

Dr. Arthur H. Becker, seminary professor, Columbus, OH

Mrs. Barbara Bue, nurse, Milwaukee, WI

Dr. I-Cheng Chang, physician, Jackson Heights, NY

Mrs. E. Corinne Chilstrom, nurse, Edina, MN

Dr. Clyde J. Christmas III, social service administrator, Jamestown, NY

Dr. Victor A. Constein, church executive, St. Louis, MO

Mrs. Joanne Dahlin, nurse, Green Bay, WI

The Rev. Warren Davis, parish pastor, Pensacola, FL

The Rev. Clarence K. Derrick, Jr., parish pastor, Newton, NC

Dr. Richard C. Dickinson, church executive, St. Louis, MO

Dr. Thomas A. Droege, university professor, Valparaiso, IN

Mr. Charles W. Dull, executive, Appleton, WI

The Rev. Jerome W. Dykstra, chaplain, Ann Arbor, MI

Mrs. Barbara Edmiston, social service administrator, Camp Hill, PA

Dr. Sandra R. Edwardson, nurse-educator, Minneapolis, MN

Mr. E. Stanley Enlund, business executive, Chicago, IL

The Rev. Frederick E. Erson, social service administrator, New Canaan, CT

The Rev. LeRoy Flagstad, parish pastor, Sioux Falls, SD

Dr. William H. Foege, physician/Assistant Surgeon General, Atlanta, GA

The Rev. Carl W. Folkemer, parish pastor, Baltimore, MD

Dr. Mark Frampton, physician, Williamson, NY

Mr. Lyle Franzen, university professor, Valparaiso, IN

Ms. Naomi Frost, publications editor, New York, NY

Mr. Sanford Fuglestad, social service administrator, Moorhead, MN

The Rev. Dale G. Gatz, social service administrator, Jacksonville, FL

Dr. Kieth A. Gerberding, parish pastor, Southgate, MI

Dr. Ruth M. Goehle, physician, St. Paul, MN

The Rev. Paul F. Goetting, consultant, Naperville, IL

The Rev. Richard J. Hafer, social service administrator, Venice, FL

Dr. David E. Harrell, Jr., university professor, Birmingham, AL

Dr. John C. Heffelfinger, physician, Watertown, WI

The Rev. Joel Hempel, parish pastor/chaplain, Cincinnati, OH

Dr. Harold J. Hinrichs, church executive, Minneapolis, MN

The Rev. Lester M. Hoffmann, church executive, Phoenix, AZ

The Rev. Larry Holst, chaplain/administrator, Park Ridge, IL

Dr. Richard F. Huegli, social services executive, Detroit, MI

Dr. Robert D. Hurlbut, parish pastor, Austin, TX
Dr. Lloyd Jacobson, dentist, Kenyon, MN
The Rev. Paul B. Janke, social service consultant, Sacramento, CA
The Rev. Arthur W. Johnson, chaplain, Fargo, ND
Ms. Barbara E. Johnson, church executive, New York, NY
The Rev. Raymond R. Johnson, social service administrator, Bayside, NY
Dr. James L. Karel, physician, Wheat Ridge, CO
Deaconess Donna King, social service administrator, Lubbock, TX
Dr. William H. Kohn, church president, Milwaukee, WI
Mr. Harold L. Kuehn, church executive, Janesville, WI
The Rev. Richard Kuehn, parish pastor/consultant, Durham, NC
The Rev. Donald H. Larsen, church executive, New York, NY
The Rev. Robert F. Lorenz, parish pastor, Vinton, IA
The Rev. Paul R. Martens, parish pastor/chaplain, Memphis, TN
Ms. Wilma M. Martens, social services administrator, Corte Madera, CA
The Rev. Lowell H. Mays, educator/clergyman, Madison, WI
Dr. Rus McCarter, consultant/clergyman, Greensboro, NC
Dr. Christian F. Midelfort, psychiatrist/educator/consultant, LaCrosse, WI
Dr. Roland E. Miller, professor/dean, Regina, Sask.
The Rev. Wallace F. Misterek, parish pastor, Olympia, WA
The Rev. William G. Moldwin, church executive, Detroit, MI
Mrs. Florence C. Montz, nurse/church executive, Bismarck, ND
The Rev. Charles S. Mueller, parish pastor, Roselle, IL
Mrs. Elizabeth Mulbah, nurse/administrator, Monrovia, Liberia
Dr. Al John Murdock, church executive, New York, NY
The Rev. Jerome Nilssen, parish pastor, Milwaukee, WI
Dr. J. A. O. Preus, church president, St. Louis, MO
Mr. Neal F. Rabe, business executive, Chicago, IL
Mrs. Sharon Raquet, nurse, North Olmsted, OH
Ms. Ruth Reko, social service administrator, St. Louis, MO
The Rev. Richard W. Rhyne, church executive, New York, NY
The Rev. Bruno F. Rieth, church executive, Porto Alegre, Brazil
Mrs. Lois Rosenberg, homemaker, Wausau, WI
Dr. Reuben J. Schmidt, parish pastor, Cincinnati, OH
The Rev. John D. Serkland, pastoral counsellor, Richmond, IN
The Rev. Fred L. Shilling, chaplain, Dallas, TX
Dr. Harvey Stalwick, university professor, Regina, Sask.
Dr. David T. Stein, educator/administrator, Park Ridge, IL
The Rev. Paul H. Strege, administrator/clergyman, St. Louis, MO
Mr. Lee Strouse, editor/graphics consultant, Addison, IL
Dr. Sharon Telleen, university professor, Washington, DC
The Rev. Delbert I. Thies, chaplain, Jacksonville, IL
Mrs. Muriel Threinen, executive director, Winnipeg, Manitoba
Dr. Paul F. Tillquist, college professor, St. Peter, MN
Dr. Richard L. Torgerson, college professor, Seguin, TX

Dr. Arthur R. Traugott, psychiatrist, Urbana, IL

Dr. Donald A. Tubesing, clergyman/psychologist, Duluth, MN

Mr. Aron A. Valleskey, church executive, Ann Arbor, MI

Dr. J. C. Vijayan, physician/hospital administrator, Wandoor, India

The Rev. Daniel J. Vinge, chaplain, LaCrosse, WI

Ms. Loretta Walker, nurse/administrator, Nicoma Park, OK

Ms. Audrey Weeks, homemaker/educator, Malverne, NY

The Rev. Susan K. Wendorf, campus pastor, Platteville, WI

Dr. Granger Westberg, clergyman/educator/consultant, Hinsdale, IL

Ms. Jill Westberg, communications/social work student, Hinsdale, IL

Dr. Orval Westby, social service executive, Minneapolis, MN

Deaconess E. Louise Williams, deaconess executive, Valparaiso, IN

The Rev. Allen S. Wysocki, parish pastor, Glen Rock, PA

Dr. Herbert Zorn, parish pastor, Portland, OR

Wheat Ridge Foundation staff members:
   Mr. Robert J. L. Zimmer, president
   Dr. Robert P. Hopmann, vice president
   Ms. Phyllis N. Kersten, communications director
   Ms. Juanita B. Tryman, secretary